The Music Box Songbook

Over 100 songs for children, compiled by Barry Gibson

CONTENTS

Published at the request of the Educational Broadcasting Council for the United Kingdom by BBC Books, a division of BBC Enterprises Limited, Woodlands, 80 Wood Lane, London W12 0TT.
First published 1987.
© BBC Enterprises Limited 1987.

ISBN 0 563 21343 4

Printed in England by Ebenezer Baylis, Worcester.

The Music Box Songbook

Doing Songs

Songs about me and you

Songs about people

Foreword

The Music Box has been opening and closing its lid for some years now, but it seems to keep springing surprises! The hinges squeak a bit, and there are creaks and grumbles hiding in the corners, but you can be sure of hearing something new and different every time.

For your young children it offers an instant and fun way of learning to join in with both traditional folk songs (from Britain and all parts of the world), and simple, modern songs, close to their own experiences, with a sprinkling of music-games and activities to build up confidence and listening skills.

How to use this Songbook

No special musical training is needed – it's for use by all parents, playgroup-leaders and teachers. As your children grow, they will be able to follow some of the words and tunes from the book themselves.

Music Box songs offer a real bridge between home, playgroups and schools. They can be as private as you like, but can also help to break the social ice, and really help youngsters become part of a new social group.

In nursery and infant schools, and for some lower juniors too, the Songbook is a rich storehouse for group and class singing, assembly ideas, projects and creative groupwork.

Use the Music Box Songbook cassette, if you like. If you can play your own accompaniments, the children will greatly appreciate this (see page 6). But most of the songs are quite happy unaccompanied. Start with those songs that most appeal to you, so that your enjoyment rubs off. Now and again, why not be daring too!

Lots of the songs are chosen to help develop vocabulary and language. You can easily lead the children from them to word-games and stories and even turn some songs into home-made reading books, perhaps asking your children to supply the pictures.

Above all, just enjoy the songs together. Don't try too many at one time – little and often is best – and remember music is for sharing, and for everyone!

Helping children sing

We can all sing, in our hearts, or with our voices, or if we're lucky, with both. Our voice is a cheap, very portable instrument, but sometimes needs help to unlock itself. There are a few simple things adults can do to make this easier for young children:

Join in, whenever you can, and make each singing session comfortable, relaxed and enjoyable. Bring everyone close together, as you would for a story. Discourage any shouting or 'sloppy' singing, but remember that the song's spirit and mood are far more important than polished diction or precise breathing. Lots of adult praise and 'positive reinforcement' really boosts confidence.

If the song seems too high or low for your children, move it up or down in pitch until it feels right (see page 6). Should any children have difficulty singing 'in tune', sit them next to someone with a good sense of pitch. You'll find that many children catch on and remember tunes much more easily than adults!

Most Music Box songs can be adapted to different age and ability levels. Just joining in the chorus may be right for one group, while slightly older children may sing (and remember!) the words of all the verses, but don't expect this. Point out the 'repeating' bits, whether choruses, odd phrases, or word-patterns. These will help everyone not to get lost, and most songs have at least one 'easy line'.

When talking about a song, try to relate it to the children's own experience, to help them make it 'their own'. In lots of cases, you can add new verses, names and phrases of your own, together. Explain any tricky words and ideas, and where possible, allow the children to choose their favourite songs to sing.

Forget the words sometimes and try just humming or singing 'la', 'moo', or whatever sounds or nonsense-words take your fancy. If there are actions, make these a real part of the singing. To help a song come alive, there's usually some scope for claps, finger-clicks or tapping on all parts of your body (see pages 122–3).

Have a few instruments handy for picking out word-rhythms and patterns. Talk often about where a tune goes *up* or *down*, *high* or *low*, and *fast* or *slow*, perhaps making the shape of a phrase in the air, with your hands.

Many Music Box songs are ready-made games and many more can easily be turned into games. Give the children plenty of chances to follow up the song ideas through painting, making things and every kind of activity that will let them carry the song around, in their heads and their hearts!

Accompaniments

If in doubt, don't! Many of our Music Box songs need very little accompaniment and often just an unaccompanied voice singing along is the best support you can give your children. 'Doubling' the melody on any melodic instrument may help them to sing in pitch, and for a fuller backing you can use our suggested chords as a basic guide.

Guitarists will find a reference chord-chart on *page 124*, and we have also given some suggested plucking patterns for certain songs in tablature. This is a simple system where lines represent strings, and numbers frets, so that:

shows a chord of G played from bass up to treble strings. Don't feel tied to these suggestions. Make up your own versions either strumming in a rhythm that suits you, or plucking to *oom-cha* or *oom-cha-cha* patterns, or breaking-up the chords into regular 'arpeggio' patterns, e.g.:

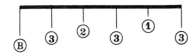

(Here, ③, ② and ① are string numbers, and Ⓑ indicates any suitable bass-string.) You can experiment with similar patterns on guitar or other plucked instruments such as banjo, ukelele, zither or celtic harp (available in kit form quite cheaply).

To change key on guitar, a 'capo' is invaluable for raising pitch to suit children's voices, or to make fingering easier for you. You can easily make a 'clock' to work out key-changes for any instrument, putting note-names (including sharps and flats) around the face, instead of the twelve numbers.

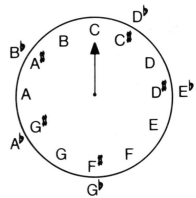

To convert a song from, say, C to E, simply move each chord four steps (clockwise) around the face, and pencil in your 'new' chords next to the originals. Remember that 'm' stands for 'minor'; also any 7's or 6's etc., but don't be afraid to simplify, if some chords are tricky for your fingers.

The autoharp is another folk instrument well worth trying. It has easy press-button chords and a rich, full sound, full of rhythmic possibilities. Also the appalachian dulcimer (available in kit form), which plays a melody and drone while perched on your knee. And have you tried any of the various squeezeboxes – concertina, melodeon and accordion – whose friendly huffing and puffing really helps children to become involved? (*See page 126*.)

Piano players can try either of the following tactics, or a combination, to suit their ability level and a particular song, but remember that a loud piano can be a barrier between you and the children. So, softly, softly . . .

- Chords alone (right-hand or left-hand), 'vamped' in rhythm, or broken into flowing 'arpeggios' or in *oom-cha* or *oom-cha-cha* patterns (*see above*).

- Melody in right-hand, simple bass-part in left-hand following chord-names (perhaps filling in with 'runs' or other notes from that chord).

These will, of course, also work for electronic keyboard instruments of many kinds too.

Children's instruments to buy

Here is a selection to think of, though you will only need a very few to capture your children's imagination. Keeping different 'music boxes' for each type will help build up an understanding of how instruments work. Remind the children that, if they're to be used again, we need to treat them with great care, always putting them down gently, almost as if each one was an egg!

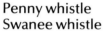

Blow

Recorder
Melodica
Pan-pipes

Penny whistle
Swanee whistle

Bamboo pipes
Kazoo (*hum*)

Tap

Drums (eg bongos)
Woodblock
Finger-cymbals
Triangle
Slit-drum

Tambour
Temple-blocks
Castanets
Cymbals

Tambourine
Indian bells
Claves
Tam-tam

Shake and rattle

Tambourine
Sleigh-bells

Cabassa
Small bells
  (eg *budgie etc.*)

Jingles
Maracas

Scrape

Guiro (*wood*)   Guiro (*metal*)   Washboard

With Strings

Ukelele   Zither   Guitar
Autoharp   Fiddle (eg ¾ *size*)

(With all these, stress the need for safety, especially avoiding any sharp wires and leaving adults to turn the tuning pegs ‗ snapping strings can be dangerous!)

Pitched

Glockenspiel
  (*metal*)
Chime-bars
  (*plus beaters*)

Xylophone
  (*wood*)
Small electronic
  keyboards

Metallophone

Cheap toy instruments

Kazoos
Sirens
Squeezers

Harmonicas
  (*mouth-organs*)
Whistles

Animal-bleaters
Squeakers
Pan-pipes

These are a useful supplement, and often ideal for music-games.

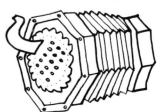

Make Music Box shakers

Try making these from card of different thicknesses, to get different sound-qualities. You can experiment with various fillings, eg pulses (chick-peas, lentils etc.), nuts and bolts. Gluing or taping the tabs and edges is fiddly so some adult help is necessary!

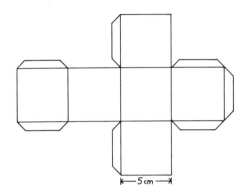

If they are very successful, add some handles, cover with papier-mâché, decorate and varnish. Decorated yoghurt-pots also make quick maracas.

Instruments to make together

The improvising spirit can turn many household objects into fascinating sound-makers. The kitchen is a good starting-storehouse: pots, pans, tins, boxes and bottles offer a rich array of wonderful sounds, but not *too* many at a time! And watch for safety. Spoons, washboards and chopsticks all have special techniques: experiment together.

Encourage your children to experiment often with everyday materials (paper, tin, plastic, key-bunches etc.), listening for their sound-qualities. You can make beaters from different kinds of material (wood, cork, cheap rubber or plastic balls, metal, even plasticine), using dowel or chopsticks for the sticks.

Here are a few ideas for instruments, to help increase your stock.

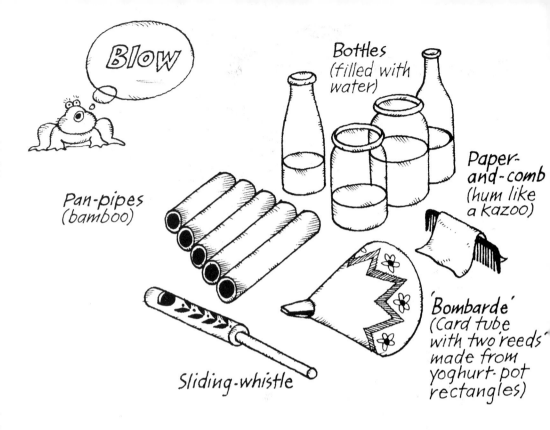

Blow

Bottles (filled with water)

Pan-pipes (bamboo)

Paper-and-comb (hum like a kazoo)

'Bombarde' (Card tube with two 'reeds' made from yoghurt-pot rectangles)

Sliding-whistle

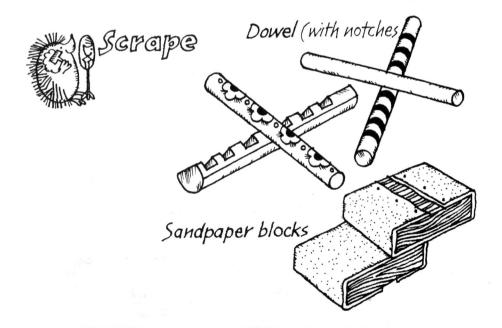

Scrape

Dowel (with notches)

Sandpaper blocks

Shake and rattle

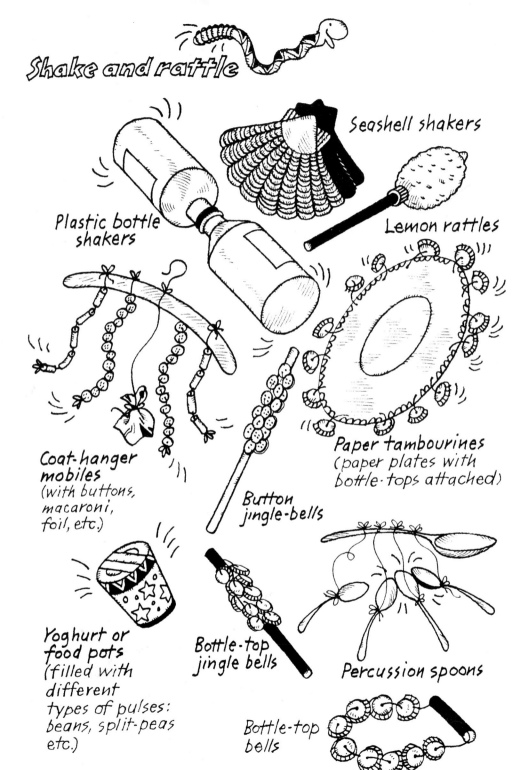

Seashell shakers

Plastic bottle shakers

Lemon rattles

Coat-hanger mobiles (with buttons, macaroni, foil, etc.)

Button jingle-bells

Paper tambourines (paper plates with bottle-tops attached)

Yoghurt or food pots (filled with different types of pulses: beans, split-peas etc.)

Bottle-top jingle bells

Percussion spoons

Bottle-top bells

Tap

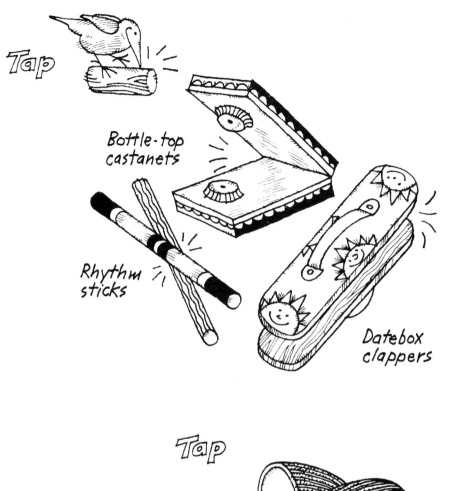

Bottle-top castanets

Rhythm sticks

Datebox clappers

Tap

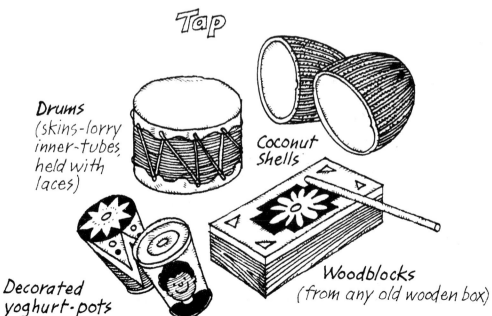

Drums (skins-lorry inner-tubes, held with laces)

Coconut Shells

Woodblocks (from any old wooden box)

Decorated yoghurt-pots

Make your own music box

You can easily make a cheap and sturdy music box for your home, classroom or playgroup from one sheet (8′ × 4′) of chipboard, or any other timber. Most large D-I-Y shops will band-saw to order free-of-charge, and we suggest these dimensions:

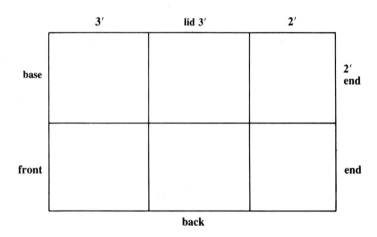

Have each edge of the base trimmed by the timber width (½″ is adequate); also the sides and bottom of each end. To fix the pieces together you will need:

> 8 plastic chipboard joints
> 2 hinges for the lid
> a catch
> a padlock and piece of string (optional)
> a few chipboard screws.

Don't forget to sandpaper any sharp edges. If you wish, you can decorate by painting (use eggshell or acrylic paint, but check for lead content) or by sticking on pictures and covering with polyurethane varnish.

Use the box for storing instruments and sound-objects safely. You could add compartments for each type of instrument or, if your collection has really grown, several music boxes.

Music skills for under-7's

Some guidelines – What to look for – What to do

Here is a *very* rough outline of early musical development. Don't worry if you think your child isn't 'keeping up'; everyone is different and the main thing about picking up music is 'Are you enjoying it?' So always be prepared to go 'back' to activities which you may think are 'too young' for your children.

0+

Up to about eighteen months, your baby or toddler will enjoy lots of rhythmic movement, so play plenty of games together which have bouncing, swaying, holding, rocking and rolling. 'Singing' phrases to each other is an excellent way of encouraging early language, so chants with silly words and on-the-knee riding games are both beneficial and fun. Keep a space in the kitchen for hitting, banging and pounding some old pots and pans – be prepared for energy and volume! Any opportunities to handle and experiment with adult or children's musical instruments (if safe) and with toy ones (*see page 7*) from as early as he or she shows interest, will be invaluable.

2+

Around two, hitting and banging should begin to become quite discriminating and you can talk about *loud, soft, fast, slow* etc. He or she will begin to imitate adult actions quite accurately and to copy tempo (speed) and rhythm. Now is the time to begin giving opportunities for social singing, and to start building up a few familiar songs. Many children will know 300–1000 words and be able to manage simple sentence-structure which songs will help enormously. Try lots of finger-games, action-games and simple movement using whole body and arm movements in response to music. Many children will value a small 'personal' collection of cassette tapes.

3+

From three, nimble fingers may be able to pick out piano keys and strum strings quite well, while nimble toes may turn clumpy dancing into proper steps. Sing lots of songs with repeating-words together – he or she will handle different tempos and rhythm-patterns quite confidently – and experiment with shaking or tapping regular beats. Don't forget to allow opportunities for music as a private experience too.

4+

With much greater independence, your child will gain a more secure unaccompanied singing voice, but will also respond to gentle accompaniment (eg guitar). New social situations (playgroups, schools etc.) will make singing circle-games good ice-breakers and songs with strong choruses will give a chance to 'sing out'. Inventing new 'lyrics' and memorising old ones are quite possible, as are the ability to order and reproduce sounds, pitches and rhythm-patterns creatively to express ideas in a story. Play listening-games and make opportunities to classify sounds by source (*where*?), volume (*how loud*?), pitch (*high or low*?) and duration (*long or short*?). On pitched percussion simple ostinati will be possible, also improvisation of pentatonic tunes (*see pages 120–1*).

5+

Aim for control, accuracy and refinement in use of instruments, and encourage the memorising of simple patterns and song-snippets. Most children will 'find' their own voice about now and be able to create, record and note down tunes, song ideas, and simple sound-pictures, if helped. Listening should become much more focused and body-movement more graceful, better adapted to musical rhythm.

6+

Children will now be able to choose songs and sing sensitively, especially if you gently discourage an occasional tendency to shout. They will sense mood, content and meaning in a song and easily extend this to projects and language work of all kinds, where music will aid concentration, diction and listening-skills. Go for physically active singing games, or musical board-games using both chance and decision-making, for opportunities to invent and construct more complicated musical patterns and sound-pictures. Listening-spans will be growing, as will a sense of rhythm and understanding of pulse or 'beat'. Take every opportunity to *share* the products of music-making.

7+

You can now look for a good, light singing tone, more accuracy and more 'perfect' performance in social singing, although the private and inward effects of music are still more important than outward 'polish'. Sound-investigation can become more purposeful and systematic. Music will greatly enrich interests in other cultures, drama and role-playing. Now is a good time to think about 'taking up' instruments, but don't forget to hark back often to simple, repetitive ideas and songs. The sky's the limit!

Children with special needs

Music can be especially rewarding for 'slow learners', children with emotional problems, and physical or mental disabilities. Blind children are often very sensitive to speech and song because of their special touching and listening-skills. Deaf and partially-hearing children will love to feel vibrations with their fingers and limbs, will usually sing heartily and respond in movement to rhythmic songs, gaining enormously from the social context. Children with neuro-muscular disabilities often have excellent voice-control and very good listening abilities especially if their movements have been confined. Above all, music and song can bring together people of every description in one voice.

Here we go round the music box

Traditional British, adapted Barry Gibson

1 Here we go round the music box,
The music box, the music box,
Here we go round the music box,
This cold and frosty morning.

2 This is the way we lift the lid,
Lift the lid, lift the lid,
This is the way we lift the lid,
This cold and frosty morning.

3 This is the way we open the box,
Open the box, open the box,
This is the way we open the box,
This cold and frosty morning.

4 This is the way we listen together,
Listen together, listen together,
This is the way we listen together,
This cold and frosty morning.

5 This is the way the sounds jump out,
Sounds jump out, sounds jump out,
This is the way the sounds jump out,
This cold and frosty morning.

6 This is the way we sing out loud,
Sing out loud, sing out loud,
This is the way we sing out loud,
This cold and frosty morning.

Here's a familiar tune, which you probably all know best as 'Mulberry Bush' or 'Nuts in May'. Dance this as a circle-dance together, making up some actions for lifting the lid (*peek in!*), opening the box (*open it wide*), listening together (*hands by ears*) and so on. Better still, dance around your own real Music Box (see page 10) and make up verses and actions for your sound-makers inside.

Johnny get your hair combed

1 John-ny get your hair combed, hair combed, hair combed,

John-ny get your hair combed, just like me. John-ny get your hair combed,

hair combed, hair combed, John-ny get your hair combed, just like me.

2 Carlie get your face washed, face washed, face washed,
Carlie get your face washed, just like me.
Carlie get your face washed, face washed, face washed,
Carlie get your face washed, just like me.

3 Evan get your teeth brushed, teeth brushed, teeth brushed,
Evan get your teeth brushed, just like me.
Evan get your teeth brushed, teeth brushed, teeth brushed,
Evan get your teeth brushed, just like me.

4 Niru get your jumper on, jumper on, jumper on,
Niru get your jumper on, just like me.
Niru get your jumper on, jumper on, jumper on,
Niru get your jumper on, just like me.

5 Lily tie your shoes up, shoes up, shoes up,
Lily tie your shoes up, just like me.
Lily tie your shoes up, shoes up, shoes up,
Lily tie your shoes up, just like me.

Don't forget some brushing, washing and dressing
actions. Make up some new verses too!

Oats and Beans

Traditional British, adapted Barry Gibson

Another well-known circle-song for skipping and dancing. Don't forget to add stamps, claps, turning around and viewing the lands (*peering*) in verse 2, allowing an extra bar's rest each time, to fit in each action.

Try making actions and sounds for new verses about 'We rake the soil' or 'We hope for rain' (*cross your fingers*), or 'We nod our heads', or 'We click our fingers'.

You can also make a 'cumulative' song by adding new pairs of food-plants to the ones mentioned in verse 1 when you reach ＊→ and ←＊. Gradually build up a list, as if you were going shopping, and see how many you can remember together, eg:

'Oats and beans, and fruits and nuts, and apples and pears, and peas and greens, and barley grows . . .' Phew!

Find out who eats which kind of breakfast cereal. Talk about the plants they are made from (maize, rice, wheat, oats, etc.). Look at how these are rolled, or flaked, or puffed. You could have a cereal guessing-game in which some small cardboard music-boxes (see page 8) are filled with different kinds of cereal. Just from shaking, can *you* guess what's in the box? _____ Flakes, perhaps, or _____ Crispies? Or maybe . . . . Porridge?!
Use words like *crunchy*, *rattle*, *bumpy*, *light*, *heavy*, *crumbly* and *sticky* to talk about the sounds.

1 Oats and beans and barley grows,
Oats and beans and barley grows.
Nor you, nor I, nor anyone knows
How oats and beans and barley grows.

Waiting for an answer.

2 Growers all, we sow the seeds.
Then we give them all they need.
We stamp our feet, We clap our hands,
We turn around, We view the lands.

Waiting for an answer.

If I were a fair one

Traditional Irish

1 If I were a fair one, fair-er than a-ny, O, I'd
marry a *car-pen-ter* be-fore I'd mar-ry a-ny, O. For
he'd *chip*, I'd *chip*, We'd *chip* to-ge-ther, O. And
what a jol-ly time we'd have, *Chip-ping* one a-no-ther, O!

1 If I were a fair one, fairer than any, O,
I'd marry a *carpenter* before I'd marry any, O.
For he'd *chip*, I'd *chip*, we'd *chip* together, O.
And what a jolly time we'd have, *chipping* one another, O!

2 If I were a fair one, fairer than any, O.
I'd marry a *tailor* before I'd marry any, O.
For he'd *stitch*, I'd *stitch*, we'd *stitch* together, O.
And what a jolly time we'd have, *stitching* one another, O!

3 If I were a fair one, fairer than any, O.
I'd marry a *sailor* before I'd marry any, O.
For he'd *row*, I'd *row*, we'd *row* together, O.
And what a jolly time we'd have, *rowing* one another, O!

Try to keep the actions for this song as steady and
rhythmic as you can. Have a go at:
   chiselling, hammering or sawing   (verse 1)
   stitching   (verse 2)
   rowing   (verse 3)
Why not make up verses and actions for other
occupations, eg hairdresser (*clip*), telephonist (*ring*),
or mountaineer (*climb*)? Change 'he' to 'she', if you like.

Tarry wool

Traditional English

1 Tarry wool, oh tarry wool,
Tarry wool is ill to spin.
Card it well, oh card it well,
Card it well ere you begin.

2 When it's carded, wove and spun,
Then your work is nearly done:
But when it's woven, dressed and clean,
It'll be clothing for a queen.

3 Up, you shepherds, dance and skip,
O'er the hills and valleys trip.
Sing in the praise of tarry wool,
And of the flock that bears it too.

Click go the shears

1 Down by the pen, there the old shear-er stands,

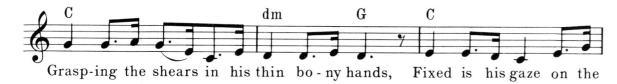

Grasp-ing the shears in his thin bo-ny hands, Fixed is his gaze on the

next sheep to come, In a lit-tle min-ute boys, a-no-ther's done.

Chorus

Click go the shears, boys, Click, click, click. Wide is his blow and his

hands move so quick. The ring-er looks a-round and is

beat-en by a blow, Zip! A-no-ther sheep is done and let him go.

1 Down by the pen, there the old shearer stands,
Grasping the shears in his thin bony hands,
Fixed is his gaze on the next sheep to come,
In a little minute boys, another's done.

Chorus:
Click go the shears, boys, Click, click, click.
Wide is his blow and his hands move so quick.
The ringer looks around and is beaten by a blow,
Zip! Another sheep is done and let him go.

2 Out on the floor in his cane bottomed chair,
There sits the boss with his eyes everywhere,
Notes well each fleece as it comes to the screen,
Paying strict attention that it's taken clean.

Chorus

3 There is the tar-boy awaiting command
With his black tar-pot and his black tarry hands.
See! One old sheep with a cut on its back.
Here is what he's waiting for,
    it's tar here, Jack.

Chorus

Sheep seem to keep turning up in the Music Box. It must be the central bleating that keeps it warm! How many woollen clothes do you have?

The words of *Click go the Shears* are a bit tricky but the chorus is fun. Reassure the children that the shears don't hurt the sheep too much. In each chorus, they will enjoy making 'scissors' with their fingers for each 'click click click' and a long 'zzzzip' from their knees to their chin.

The cockle gatherer

Different kinds and sizes of seashell can be filled with sand, or tiny shells, for 'seashell shakers'. In *The Cockle Gatherer* see what other phrases you can make instead of 'Laughter of sea waves', eg 'Swish of the shingle'.

Three Jolly Fishermen works well with actions (*heave, throw, pull* etc.), especially if you make new verses to turn it into a story, with splashing oars, crabs, and other surprises in their nets!

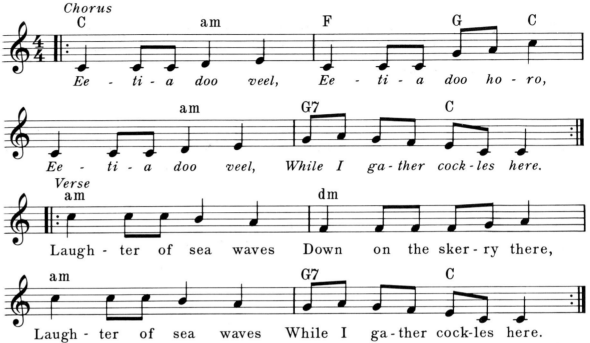

Chorus

Ee - ti - a doo veel, Ee - ti - a doo ho - ro,
Ee - ti - a doo veel, While I ga - ther cock - les here.

Verse

Laugh - ter of sea waves Down on the sker - ry there,
Laugh - ter of sea waves While I ga - ther cock - les here.

Chorus:
Eetia doo veel,
Eetia doo horo,
Eetia doo veel,
While I gather cockles here. (Sing twice)

Laughter of sea waves
Down on the skerry there,
Laughter of sea waves
While I gather cockles here. *(Sing twice)*

Chorus

There were three jolly fishermen

Traditional English

There were three jol-ly fish-er-men and they put out to sea.— There

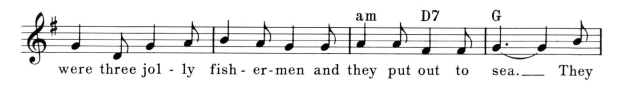

were three jol-ly fish-er-men and they put out to sea.— They

threw their nets in-to the sea and pulled them out by one, two, three, To

see what they had got, had got, to see what they had got.—

There were three jolly fishermen and they put out to sea.
There were three jolly fishermen and they put out to sea.
They threw their nets into the sea
And pulled them out by one, two, three,
To see what they had got, had got, to see what they had got.

Banyan tree

Traditional Jamaican

1 Moonshine tonight, come make we dance and sing,
Moonshine tonight, come make we dance and sing

Chorus:
Me do rock so, you do rock so,
Under banyan tree.
Me do rock so, you do rock so,
Under banyan tree.

2 Ladies make curtsey and gentlemen make bow,
Ladies make curtsey and gentlemen make bow.

Chorus:
Me do rock so, you do rock so,
Under banyan tree.
Me do rock so, you do rock so,
Under banyan tree.

3 Then we join hands an' dance around an' around
Then we join hands an' dance around an' around.

Chorus:
Me do rock so, you do rock so,
Under banyan tree.
Me do rock so, you do rock so,
Under banyan tree.

A banyan is a kind of fig tree with enormous, spreading roots.

This song is fun to sing in a circle. For each chorus, rock and clap from side to side. In verse 1, circle to the left. In verse 2, curtsey or bow to your partner. In verse 3, circle to the right.

Work calypso

1 Ma - ma says no play, This is a work day,

Up with the bright sun, Get all the work done. If you will help me

Climb up the tall tree, Shake the pa - pa - ya down.

Tap this rhythm together:

Ma-ma says no play

Then try it on tapping, shaking or scraping instruments (see pages 8–9 and 42–43) and experiment with other rhythm-patterns to help the Calypso rhythm. You could add actions for *getting up, climbing, washing dishes, running* and *picking up.* Then think up some verses of your own for things *you* might do to help in the home.

Guitar Tab (Capo at III)

etc.

1 Mama says no play,
This is a work day,
Up with the bright sun,
Get all the work done.

If you will help me
Climb up the tall tree,
Shake the papaya down.

2 Mama says no play,
This is a work day,
Up with the bright sun,
Get all the work done.

If you will help me
Wash up the dishes,
Stack them up one, two, three.

3 Mama says no play,
This is a work day,
Up with the bright sun,
Get all the work done.

If you will help me
Run to the market,
Bring me some ripe ackee.

4 Mama says no play,
This is a work day,
Up with the bright sun,
Get all the work done.

If you will help me
Pick all your toys up,
Put them back tidily.

Jump shamador

Another ring game where the 'mother' (or 'father') walks round the outside to choose a 'daughter' (or 'son'). This parent shakes their head and stamps their foot for 'can't', while the child mimes actions for their chosen occupation. For both songs, make up new verses for what you would like to be.

Good morn-ing to you, daugh-ter. Good morn-ing to you, mo-ther.

What is your in-tent-ion? I want to be a *teach-er.* You

can't be a *teach-er.* I must be a *teach-er.*

Chorus

Jump sha-ma-dor my dar-ling   *Jump sha-ma-dor my dear.*

(whisper)

Jump sha-ma-dor, Jump sha-ma-dor, Jump sha-ma-dor, Jump sha-ma-dor.

I want to be a farmer . . .

I want to be a dancer . . .

I want to be a doctor . . .

Make up new verses for what *you* would like to be.

22

Chicka hanka

Traditional North American, adapted Barry Gibson

1 Captain, go side-track your train.
Chicka hanka Chicka hanka
Captain, go side-track your train.
Chicka hanka Chicka hanka
Number three in line,
Comin' in on time,
Captain, go side-track your train.

2 Driver, go start up your bus.
Chicka hanka Chicka hanka
Driver, go start up your bus.
Chicka hanka Chicka hanka
Number seventy-eight,
Twenty minutes late,
Driver, go start up your bus.

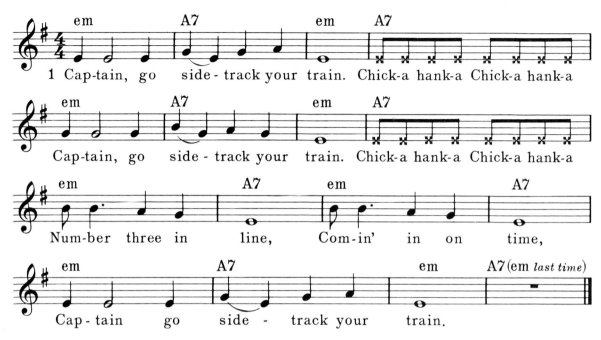

3 Dancer, go do your exercises.
Chicka hanka Chicka hanka
Dancer, go do your exercises.
Chicka hanka Chicka hanka
When it's half past ten,
Do them all again,
Dancer, go do your exercises.

4 Gardener, go dig up those worms.
Chicka hanka Chicka hanka
Gardener, go dig up those worms.
Chicka hanka Chicka hanka
Rest at half past three,
For a cup of tea,
Gardener, go dig up those worms.

5 Tailor, go stitch up that suit.
Chicka hanka Chicka hanka
Tailor, go stitch up that suit.
Chicka hanka Chicka hanka
Working through the night,
Keep those stitches tight,
Tailor, go stitch up that suit.

I want to be a driver . . .

Don't forget to do some actions!

Keep on dancing

Words: Judy Farrar, Janice Honeyman, Katrina Noble
Music: Harriet Powell

Keep on dancing, Keep on dancing, Keep on singing this song. Keep on dancing, Keep on dancing, Keep on singing this song.

1 Clap your hands and stamp your feet.

Wiggle your eyebrows to the beat. Wiggle your eyebrows, wiggle your eyebrows. Keep on singing this song.

↦ *Repeat as necessary*

2 Clap your hands and stamp your feet.
Shake your shoulders to the beat.
Shake your shoulders, shake your shoulders,
Wiggle your eyebrows, wiggle your eyebrows,
Keep on singing this song.

Chorus

3 Clap your hands and stamp your feet.
Knobble your kneecaps to the beat.
Knobble your kneecaps, knobble your kneecaps,
Shake your shoulders, shake your shoulders,
Wiggle your eyebrows, wiggle your eyebrows,
Keep on singing this song.

Chorus

4 Clap your hands and stamp your feet.
Wobble your bottom to the beat.
Wobble your bottom, wobble your bottom,
Knobble your kneecaps, knobble your kneecaps,
Shake your shoulders, shake your shoulders,
Wiggle your eyebrows, wiggle your eyebrows,
Keep on singing this song.

So do I!

Words and Music: Sandra Kerr

Chorus — G — am — G

Some things I like, some things I hate, Some things are fun to
And if with me you all a-gree, Then come on don't be

D7 — G — am — D7 — G

do And all these some things, All these fun things I'll tell you.
shy, Af-ter each thing I sing, you sing 'So do I'.

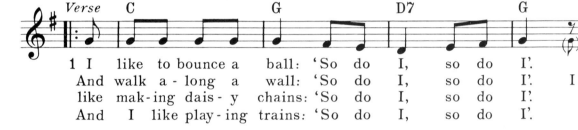

Verse — C — G — D7 — G

1 I like to bounce a ball: 'So do I, so do I'.
And walk a-long a wall: 'So do I, so do I'. I
like mak-ing dais-y chains: 'So do I, so do I'.
And I like play-ing trains: 'So do I, so do I'.

Chorus

2 I like making pies with mud –   So do I, so do I
Chips and beans and chocolate pud – So do I, so do I
I like standing on my head –   So do I, so do I
But I hate to go to bed! –   So do I, so do I

Chorus

3 I like jumping over ditches –   So do I, so do I
Reading stories about witches –   So do I, so do I
Playing football in the park –   So do I, so do I
Hide and Seek in the dark! –   So do I, so do I

Chorus

4 I like sliding, I like swinging –   So do I, so do I
I like shouting, I like singing –   So do I, so do I
In my wellies I like splashing –   So do I, so do I
What I *really* hate is WASHING! –   So do I, so do I

What are *your* favourite things to do?

25

Try again

Words and Music: Sandra Kerr

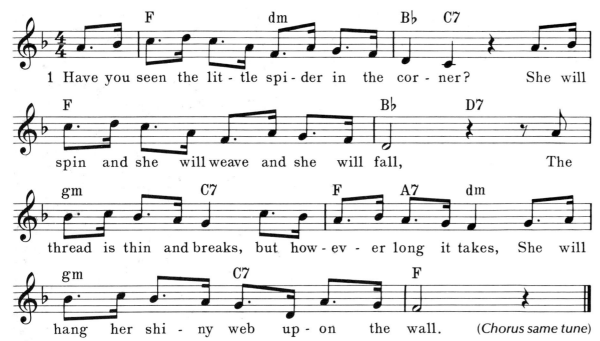

1 Have you seen the lit-tle spi-der in the cor-ner? She will
spin and she will weave and she will fall, The
thread is thin and breaks, but how-ev-er long it takes, She will
hang her shi-ny web up-on the wall. *(Chorus same tune)*

Chorus:
So I'll imitate the spider in the corner,
If at first I don't succeed I'll try again.
Though the way is very long,
I will say, when things go wrong,
If I try I'm bound to get there in the end.

2 Think about the salmon from the ocean:
They must swim against the tide and stand the test,
Leaping rocks and water falls,
Through streams and icy pools,
Till, in gentle rivers, they can take their rest.

Chorus

3 Remember too, the swallows in the sunshine:
Halfway round the world they have to fly,
Blown by stormy winds and rain,
But they'll do it all again,
To soar into a blue and summer sky.

Chorus

The tidy song

Words and Music: Sandra Kerr

1 What will you do to-day to keep the play-ground ti - dy?

Come a-long, sur-prise me, What 'll you do to-day? I'll pick

up the sweet-ie pa-per if it's ly-ing on the ground, And I'll

put it ve-ry ti - di-ly a - way.

1 What will you do today to keep the *playground* tidy?
Come along, surprise me: what'll you do today?
I'll pick up the sweetie paper if it's lying on the ground,
And I'll put it very tidily away.

2 What will you do today to keep the *park* tidy?
Come along, surprise me: what'll you do today?
I'll pick up an empty beer can if it's lying on the grass,
And I'll put it very tidily away.

3 What will you do today to keep *your bedroom* tidy?
Come along, surprise me: what'll you do today?
I'll pick up my bedroom slippers if they're lying on the floor,
And I'll put them very tidily away.

Can you make up verses about the *Garden*?
Or the *Bathroom*?

Don't bother me

Words and Music: Malvina Reynolds

1 Don't bother me, I have some things to do,
Don't bother me, I have to tie my shoe,
Don't bother me, I'm standing like a tree,
Spin like a top, I can't stop,
Don't bother me.

2 Don't bother me, I have to hurry by,
Don't bother me, I'm learning how to fly,
Don't bother me, I'm buzzing like a bee,
Roll down the hill, can't keep still,
Don't bother me.

3 Don't bother me, I'm thinking something nice,
Don't bother me, I'm sliding on the ice,
Don't bother me, I'm singing 'Toodle-dee',
Boat on the bay, sailing away,
Don't bother me.

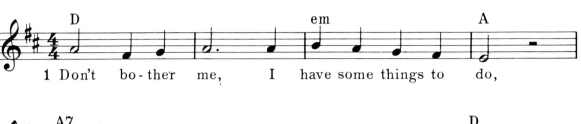

1 Don't bo-ther me, I have some things to do,

Don't bo-ther me, I have to tie my shoe,

Don't bo-ther me, I'm stand-ing like a tree,

Spin like a top, I can't stop, Don't bo-ther me.

The swing

Words: Robert Louis Stevenson
Music: Michael Burnett

How do you like to go up in a swing,

Up in the air so blue?___ Oh, I do think it the

pleas - ant - est thing ev - er a child can do.

1 How do you like to go up in a swing,
   Up in the air so blue?
   Oh, I do think it the pleasantest thing
   Ever a child can do.

2 Up in the air and over the wall,
   'Til I can see so wide,
   Rivers and trees and cattle and all,
   Over the countryside.

3 'Til I look down on the garden shed,
   Down on the roof so brown,
   Up in the air I go flying again,
   Up in the air and down.

What do you most like to do when you are spending time on your own?

29

Hair

1 Hair can be short, hair can be long. It can be fine_ or

thick_ and strong. It can be curl - y, fram-ing your face.

It can be smooth, or all o - ver the place. *Hair grows slow-ly,_*

Chorus

takes its time, Takes its time, takes its time. Hair grows slow-ly,

takes its time. You can ne-ver rush it,_ No mat-ter how you brush it._

2 Hair can be yellow, hair can be brown,
Tied up in bunches, or hanging straight down.
Hair can be black, or hair can be red,
Curled into ringlets all over your head.

Chorus

3 Tie it in ribbons. Tie it in bows.
Cut it off short and wait till it grows.
Wear it in dreadlocks. Wear it in plaits,
Or cover it over in different hats.

Chorus

4 Hair can be short, hair can be long.
It can be fine or thick and strong,
It can be curly, framing your face,
It can be smooth, or all over the place.

Chorus

Why does it have to be me?

Words and Music: Leon Rosselson

Why does it have to be me? Why can't they just let me be? Why do I have to do things I don't want to do? Why does it have to be me? 1 Each morn-ing I lie in my bed, Slip-per-y dreams in my head. I live in a fine fair-y cas-tle of stone, All on my own, no-one to moan, Then a voice shouts 'Get up!' and it is-n't a dream, 'Hur-ry up you're late for school, and wash your face and brush your teeth, and are your fin-gers clean?' And it goes on and on till I'm read-y to scream. Why does it have to be me?

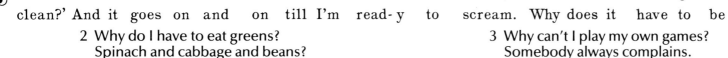

2 Why do I have to eat greens?
Spinach and cabbage and beans?
I don't mind potatoes, I'll even have meat,
Though I'd much rather eat ice-cream and sweets.

They say greens are good for me, maybe they're right,
But sometimes I think that they do it for spite,
And I've never seen them eating what they don't like.
So why does it have to be me? *Chorus*

3 Why can't I play my own games?
Somebody always complains.
Whenever I'm playing at monsters or bears,
Jumping off chairs, falling downstairs,

It's 'Don't be so noisy', or 'Go out and play',
Or 'Look at a book if you're going to stay',
But the problem is, they always get in my way,
So why does it have to be me? *Chorus*

We're going to make a circus

Words and Music: Leon Rosselson

We're go-ing to make a cir - cus, We're go ing to make a cir - cus. We're go-ing to make a cir - cus, The great-est show on earth.___ It's gi-gan-tic It's gi-gan - tic It 'll be fran - tic It 'll be fran-tic Thrill a min - ute, Thrill a min - ute, Come a - long and be in it! Come a - long and be in it!

All by yourself

Words and Music: Leon Rosselson

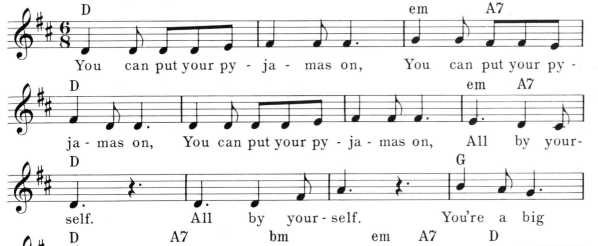

You can put your py - ja - mas on, You can put your py - ja - mas on, You can put your py - ja - mas on, All by your-self. All by your - self. You're a big girl now, You can do it, All by your - self.

Another 'Gamesong' to make up your own verses and actions. This time, lots of you could do them together, eg:

'We're going to hoist the big top (HEEEAVE!) . . .
The biggest top on earth. . . .'
or
'We're going to roar like a lion (ROARRRR!!!) . . .
The hungriest lion on earth . . .'
or
'We're going to walk the tightrope (balance toes and hands) . . .
The tightest rope on earth . . .

◄ All by Yourself

Different people do different things at different ages. If you like, change 'you' to 'I' and 'girl' to 'boy', then add your own actions and verses, eg:
'I can tie my laces . . .'
or
'I can pull my pullover over . . .'

Helping Grandma Jones

Words and Music: Jill Darby

1 Grand-ma Jones is ra-ther old, She is-n't ve-ry strong,— She

wraps up warm a-gainst the cold When win-ter comes a-long.

Chorus

Tell us how we can help you, Grand-ma Jones?

Have you some jobs we can do, Grand-ma Jones?

2 Grandma Jones lives in a flat,
   We help her up the stairs.
   We sweep the floor, we brush the mat,
   To show that someone cares.

   Chorus

3 Grandma Jones can't walk too fast
   When we go to the shop.
   We always get back home at last,
   Although we often stop.

   Chorus

4 She's very fond of girls and boys,
   Her face is always kind.
   Although we sometimes make a noise,
   She never seems to mind.

   Chorus

Guitar Tab

etc.

(G)   (D7)

The jolly miller

There was a jolly miller and he lived by himself,
As the wheel went round he made his wealth.
With one hand on the hopper and the other on his bag,
As the wheel went round he made his grab!

Can you make this song into a story by making up new verses about what happened to the miller, and his cat, and his dog?

34

Old Joe Clark

Traditional North American

1 Old Joe Clark he had a house, For-ty stor-eys high, And ev-'ry stor-ey in that house Was lined with chick-en pie.

Chorus

Fare you well, Old Joe Clark, Fare you well, I say.

Fare you well, Old Joe Clark, For I'm a-go-in' a-way.

2 I wish I had a lariat rope
  Long as I could throw,
  Throw it round my sweetheart's waist,
  And down the road we'd go.

  Chorus

3 I wish I was an apple,
  Hanging on a tree,
  Every time that pretty girl passed
  She'd take a bite of me.

  Chorus

4 Peaches in the summertime,
  Apples in the fall,
  If I can't get the girl I want
  I won't have none at all.

  Chorus

5 Never got no money,
  Got no place to stay,
  Got no place to lay my head
  And the chickens a-crowing for day.

  Chorus

Grandma Grunts

Traditional North American

1 Grand-ma Grunts said a cur-i-ous thing, 'Boys may whis-tle, but girls must sing'. That is what I heard her say, 'Twas no long-er than yes-ter-day.

Chorus

Boys can whis-tle, (whistle)............... Girls must sing, 'Tra-la - la - la - la'.

1 Grandma Grunts said a curious thing,
'Boys may whistle, but girls must sing'.
That is what I heard her say,
'Twas no longer than yesterday.

Chorus:
Boys can whistle, (whistle)
Girls must sing, 'Tra-la-la-la-la'.

2 Boys can whistle of course they may,
They can whistle the livelong day,
Why can't girls whistle too, pray tell,
If they manage to do it well?

Chorus:
Boys can whistle, (whistle)
Girls must sing, 'Tra-la-la-la-la'.

Are *you* any good at whistling? Can you think of any
other nonsense words you could sing tunes to, instead
of 'Tra-la-la-la-la'? How about 'Doo-be-doo-doo-doo',
or 'Rub-a-dub-dub-dub'?

Daughters will you marry?

Traditional North American
(adapted Barry Gibson)

1 Daugh-ters will you mar-ry? Yea, fa-ther,

yea. Will you mar-ry a farm-er? Nay, fa-ther,

nay. A farm-er's wife I will not be,

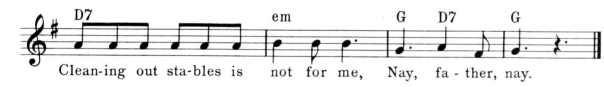

Clean-ing out sta-bles is not for me, Nay, fa-ther, nay.

1 Daughters will you marry?
Yea, father, yea.
Will you marry a farmer?
Nay, father, nay.

A farmer's wife I will not be,
Cleaning out stables is not for me.
Nay, father, nay.

2 Daughters will you marry?
Yea, father, yea.
Will you marry a fisherman?
Nay, father, nay.

A fisherman's wife I will not be.
Digging up worms is not for me.
Nay, father, nay.

3 Daughters will you marry?
Wait, father, wait.
Will you marry a fiddler?
Wait, father, wait.

Well I might be a fiddler's wife,
Singing and dancing all of my life.
Wait, father, wait.

* For now I'll just stay on the shelf
And play on the fiddle all by myself.
Wait, father, wait.

* *Repeat the music of the last three lines*

Add actions for cleaning out stables (verse 1), digging
up worms (verse 2) and playing the fiddle (verse 3).

Will you wear red?

Traditional North American

G   em   am7   D7

1 O will you wear red, O my dear, O my dear?

G   em   am7   D7   G

Will you wear red, Jen-nie Jen - kins?___ I won't wear red, it's the

C   Chorus   G

col - our of my head, I'll buy me a twir-ley-whir-ley,

soo-key-loo-key, Sal-ly Kat-ty, dou-ble-lol-ly, Roll - the-

em   G   D7   G

find-me. Roll,_____ Jen-nie Jen-kins, roll.

2 O will you wear *blue*, . . .
I won't wear *blue*, for I won't be true.

Chorus

3 O will you wear *yellow*, . . .
I won't wear *yellow*, my fine young fellow.

Chorus

4 O will you wear *green*, . . .
I won't wear *green*, I'm ashamed to be seen.

Chorus

5 O will you wear *grey*, . . .
I won't wear *grey* on a sunny day.

Chorus

6 O what will you wear, O my dear, O my dear?
What will you wear, Jennie Jenkins?
Now what do you care if I just go bare!

Chorus

The green dress

Words and Music: Josef Marais

When-e-ver Het-ty has a green dress on, green dress on, green dress on, When-

e-ver Het-ty has a green dress on, We will sing a song for her.

Let us sing a song, it need-n't be so long, For Het-ty has a green dress on!

Let us sing a song, it need-n't be so long, For Het-ty has a green dress on.

You can change the name from 'Hetty' to anyone you choose. Instead of a green dress,
why not try singing about a 'blue shirt', or an 'orange hat'?

The wedding dress song

Traditional North American

1 Hey, my little Domie gal, don't you guess?
You'd better be making your wedding dress.
Wedding dress, wedding dress,
You'd better be making your wedding dress.

2 Hey, it's already made, trimmed in brown,
Stitched around with a golden crown.
Golden crown, golden crown,
Stitched around with a golden crown.

3 Hey, it's already made, trimmed in green,
Prettiest thing you've ever seen.
Ever seen, ever seen,
Prettiest thing you've ever seen.

4 Hey, it's already made, trimmed in white,
Gonna get married on Sunday night.
Sunday night, Sunday night,
Gonna get married on Sunday night.

5 Well, she wouldn't say yes, she wouldn't say no,
All she'd do is just sit and sew.
Sit and sew, sit and sew,
All she'd do is just sit and sew.

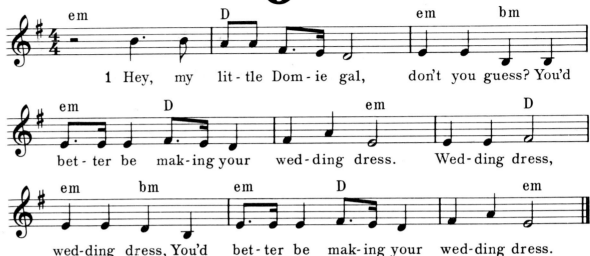

Two beautiful American melodies which only need the gentlest of accompaniments. *The Wedding Dress Song* works very well with a simple 'drone' (the note E) sustained right the way through. Children can do this on any pitched instrument (eg chime-bars), or plucking just the top and bottom open strings on a guitar.

These songs, and the previous two, will give you a lot of ideas for talking about (and experimenting with) colours.

Shady Grove

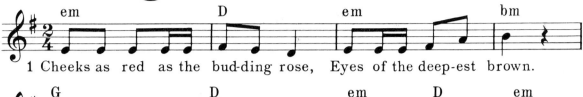

1 Cheeks as red as the bud-ding rose, Eyes of the deep-est brown.

You are the dar-ling of my heart, Stay till the sun goes down.

1 Cheeks as red as the budding rose,
Eyes of the deepest brown.
You are the darling of my heart,
Stay till the sun goes down.

Chorus:
Shady Grove, my little love,
Shady Grove, my dear,
Shady Grove, my little love,
I'm going to leave you here.

2 Shady Grove, my little love,
Standing in the door,
Shoes and stockings in her hands,
And her little bare feet on the floor.

Chorus

3 Wished I had a big fine horse,
Corn to feed him on,
Pretty little girl stay at home,
Feed him when I'm gone.

Chorus

(*Chorus same tune*)

Water come a me eye

1 Ev'ry time I think of Liza,
Water come a me eye.
Ev'ry time I think of Liza,
Water come a me eye.

Come back, Liza, come back, girl,
Water come a me eye.
Come back, Liza, come back, girl,
Water come a me eye.

2 Don't know why you went away,
Water come a me eye.
When you comin' home to stay?
Water come a me eye.

Come back, Liza, come back, girl,
Water come a me eye.
Come back, Liza, come back, girl,
Water come a me eye.

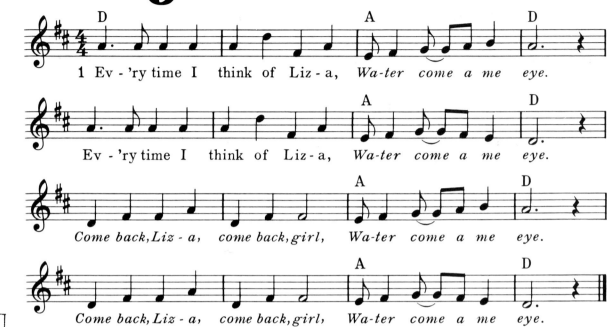

1 Ev - 'ry time I think of Liz - a, Wa-ter come a me eye.

Ev - 'ry time I think of Liz - a, Wa-ter come a me eye.

Come back, Liz - a, come back, girl, Wa-ter come a me eye.

Come back, Liz - a, come back, girl, Wa-ter come a me eye.

What kind of things make you happy or sad? Going away? Making friends?

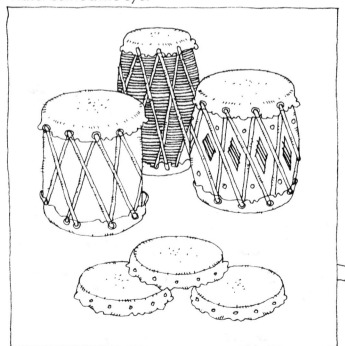

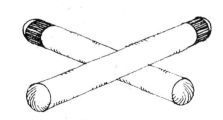

Janey gal

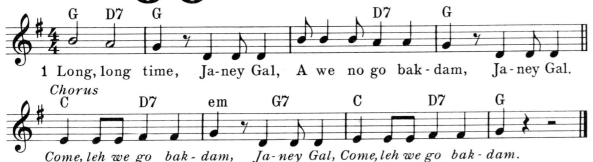

1 Long, long time, Ja-ney Gal, A we no go bak-dam, Ja-ney Gal.

Chorus

Come, leh we go bak-dam, Ja-ney Gal, Come, leh we go bak-dam.

1 Long, long time, Janey Gal,
A we no go bak-dam, Janey Gal.

Chorus:
Come leh we go bak-dam, Janey Gal,
Come leh we go bak-dam.

2 Since we cut de cane, Janey Gal,
A we no go bak-dam, Janey Gal.

Chorus

3 All dem bwoy a say, Janey Gal,
A we no go bak-dam, Janey Gal.

Chorus

4 Long, long time, Janey Gal,
A we no go bak-dam, Janey Gal.

Chorus

'Bak-dam' is a Guyanese word for a lover's lane!

Both these songs are good for gently rocking from side to side. Pick out the rhythms of key phrases to tap and say together, eg:
Water come a me eye
Come back, Liza
Come leh we go bak dam.
Then try shaking, tapping, scraping or rattling these patterns on any instruments you have available. The instruments shown here are African or Caribbean. Use bongos as well, or have a go at making some drums of your own (*see page 9*). On a xylophone try playing GDGDGDGD, over and over.

rattle

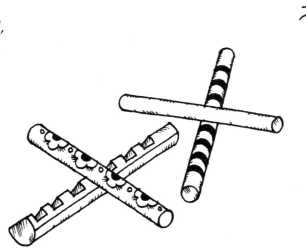

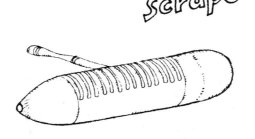

Scrape

Tap

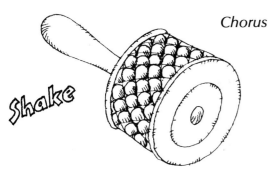

Shake

The bonny pit laddie

Traditional English

Can you make verses about other jobs or occupations?

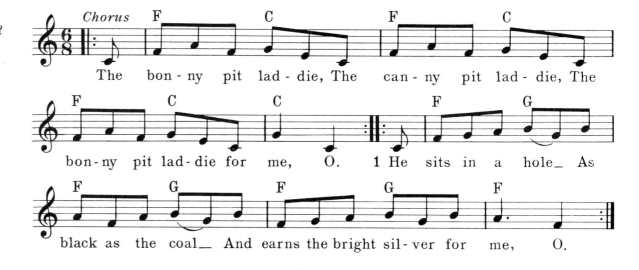

The bon - ny pit lad - die, The can - ny pit lad - die, The bon - ny pit lad - die for me, O. 1 He sits in a hole_ As black as the coal_ And earns the bright sil - ver for me, O.

Chorus:
The bonny pit laddie,
The canny pit laddie,
The bonny pit laddie for me, O.

1 He sits in a hole
  As black as the coal
  And earns the bright silver for me, O.

Chorus:
The bonny pit laddie,
The canny pit laddie,
The bonny pit laddie for me, O.

2 He sits on his cracket,
  And hews in his jacket,
  And earns the bright silver for me, O.

Chorus:
The bonny pit laddie,
The canny pit laddie,
The bonny pit laddie for me, O.

Magic penny

Words and Music: Malvina Reynolds

Chorus

Love is some-thing if you give it a-way,— give it a-way,—

give it a-way,— Love is some-thing if you give it a-way,— You

Verse

end up hav-ing more. 1 It's just like a ma-gic pen-ny,—

Hold it tight and you won't have a-ny,— Lend it spend it and you'll

have so ma-ny— they'll roll all o-ver the floor, for ....

Chorus:
Love is something if you give it away,
Give it away, give it away,
Love is something if you give it away,
You end up having more.

1 It's just like a magic penny,
  Hold it tight and you won't have any.
  Lend it, spend it and you'll have so many,
  They'll roll all over the floor, for . . .

  Chorus

2 Let's go dancing till the break of day,
  And if there's a piper, we can pay,
  For love is something if you give it away,
  You end up having more, for . . .

  Chorus

Let us come in

Words and Music: Malvina Reynolds

1 We are three wan-d'ring trav-'lers____ Out in the wind and the rain____ We saw your light, cheer-y and bright, And tapped on your win-dow-pane, sing-ing

Chorus

Let us come in, Let us come in, In-to your house so gay.____ Let us come in, Let us come in, Please do not send us a-way.____

4 Please go ahead with your dinner,
We will just wait till you're through,
But if you find there's enough to go around,
Save us a mince-pie or two, singing:

Chorus

5 We will make noise very softly,
The landlord won't hear us at all,
And if there's not enough room in the beds
We will just sleep in the hall, singing:

Chorus

6 One or two extra won't matter,
Plenty of room on the floor,
You'll look around and find we have gone
After a fortnight or more, singing:

Chorus

2 We heard the music playing,
Sounded like happy time news,
One of us said, 'Let's knock on the door!'
The other said, 'What can we lose?' singing:

Chorus

3 One of us plays on the whistle,
Makes such a musical tweet,
One of us sings such beautiful things,
And one keeps time with his feet,
 singing:

Chorus

Grandpa had a party

Words and music: Jill Darby

1 Grand-pa had a par-ty for his birth-day last night __ Ev-'ry-bo-dy had some fun 'cos It was a great one. He sat by his pi-a-no and he played it good and loud. With all the win-dows o-pen he col-lect-ed quite a crowd. *When Grand-pa had a par-ty, it was real-ly quite a game, When Grand-pa had a par-ty, ev-'ry-bo-dy came.* ___

2 Granny brought her trumpet and she gave it a toot
She played her very favourite tune and *it was a great one*,
She swung her trumpet in the air, she played it high and low,
The neighbours started coming in to hear the music show.

Chorus

3 Eric walked into the room and he joined the band
He brought his washboard in to play and *it was a great one*,
He put a thimble on his thumb and gave it all he had
Our dog ran underneath the chair, the music drove him mad.

Chorus

4 Philip brought his drum-kit and he started to play
Drummed a paradiddle, then, and *it was a great one*,
He twirled his drumsticks round and round and threw them in the air
He crashed the cymbal very loud, he didn't seem to care.

Chorus

5 And when the party finished all the neighbours went home,
And everyone who came along said *it was a great one*,
Grandpa closed the piano-lid and sent the dog to bed,
Granny put her trumpet down and turned to him and said:

Final Chorus:
'Everybody had a good time, don't you think we could
Have another party soon?' Grandpa said 'We should!'

My bonnie lies over the ocean

Traditional English

1 My bonnie lies over the ocean,
My bonnie lies over the sea,
My bonnie lies over the ocean,
O bring back my bonnie to me.

Chorus:
Bring back, bring back,
O bring back my bonnie to me, to me,
Bring back, bring back,
O bring back my bonnie to me.

2 Last night as I lay on my pillow,
Last night as I lay on my bed,
Last night as I lay on my pillow,
I dreamed that my bonnie was dead.

Chorus

3 O blow ye winds over the ocean,
O blow ye winds over the sea,
O blow ye winds over the ocean,
And bring back my bonnie to me.

Chorus

4 The winds have blown over the ocean,
The winds have blown over the sea,
The winds have blown over the ocean,
And brought back my bonnie to me.

Chorus

48

My Johnnie was a shoemaker

Traditional

1 My— John-nie was a shoe-mak - er, And clear - ly he loved me; My— John-nie was a shoe-mak - er, But— now he's gone to sea, With— nas - ty pitch to soil his hands, And sail up-on the storm-y sea;—— My— John-nie was a shoe-mak - er.——

2 His jacket was a deep sky blue,
   and curly was his hair.
His jacket was a deep sky blue,
   it was, I do declare.
To reef the topsail now he's gone,
   and sail upon the stormy sea.
My Johnnie was a shoemaker.

3 He'll be a captain by and by,
   with a brave and gallant crew.
He'll be a captain by and by,
   with a sword and spyglass too.
And when he is a captain bold,
   he'll come back to marry me.
My Johnnie was a shoemaker.

Three men went a-hunting

Traditional English

1 Three men went a-hunting, And nothing could they find,— Until they came on a hedge-hog, And that they left be-hind.— The Eng-lish-man said, 'It's a hedge-hog', The Scots-man he said 'Nay'. Taf-fy said, 'It's a pin-cush-ion with the pins stuck in the wrong way,' *And look at that now, And look at that now, Tit-ty fa-la, fa-la, fa-lay, Tit-ty fa-la, fa-lay.*

2 They went along a bit further
and nothing did they find,
Until they came on a chimney pot
and that they left behind.
The Englishman said, 'It's a chimney pot'.
The Scotsman he said 'Nay'.
Taffy said, 'It's a pipe with the mouthpiece
worn away'.

Chorus

3 They went along a bit further
and nothing did they find,
Until they came on an ostrich egg
and that they left behind;
The Englishman said, 'It's an ostrich egg'.
The Scotsman he said 'Nay'.
Taffy said, 'It's a cube of ivory with the corners
worn away!'

Chorus

4 They went along a bit further
and nothing did they find,
Until they came on an empty space
and that they left behind;
The Englishman said, 'It's an empty space'.
The Scotsman he said 'Nay'.
Taffy said, 'It's a house with the walls and
the roof and the door all worn away'.

Chorus

5 They went along a bit further and nothing did
they find,
Until they came on a Music Box . . .

We have left verse 5 for you to put in your own ideas for what the Englishman, Scotsman and Taffy had to say.

You could add some extra percussion sounds to this song, based on the rhythm of the phrase 'Titty-fa-la', or after special words in each verse.

Try scrapy sounds for the hedgehog, tapping flower-pots for chimney-pots, woodblocks or drums for the ostrich egg, and a swanee-whistle for the empty space.

The boaster

Traditional Czech, adapted Barry Gibson

Introduction

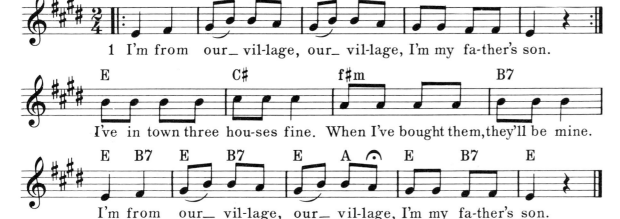

Don't believe a word he says!

1 I'm from our village, our village,
I'm my father's son.
I'm from our village, our village,
I'm my father's son.
I've in town three houses fine.
When I've bought them, they'll be mine.
I'm from our village, our village,
I'm my father's son.

2 I'm from Milton Keynes, Milton Keynes,
I'm called Sue.
I'm from Milton Keynes, Milton Keynes,
I'm called Sue.
I've a five-wheeled bike, it's true!
Front wheels (3) and back wheels (2).
I'm from Milton Keynes, Milton Keynes,
I'm called Sue.

Here's a chance for you to make up some fibs! Instead of 'our village' put the name of your town, city or village. Instead of 'my father's son', put your name. Then you can make up the craziest fib you can think of to boast about!

Uncle Joe, Scarecrow

Words and Music: Sandra Kerr

My name is Un-cle Joe, I'm an old scare-crow.

Here's the gear that I shall wear to - day.

Straw for my hair, and I call it Bar - net Fair And it

helps to keep the bird - ies all a - way.

2 . . . an old top hat, and I call it Tit-for-Tat
straw for my hair, and I call it Barnet Fair . . .

3 . . . a ragged shirt, and I call it Dicky Dirt
an old top hat and I call it Tit-for-Tat
straw for my hair, and I call it Barnet Fair . . .

4 . . . turn-up trousers, and I call them Round the Houses
a ragged shirt, and I call it Dicky Dirt
an old top hat, and I call it Tit-for-Tat
straw for my hair, and I call it Barnet Fair . . .

5 . . . a pair of welly boots, and I call them Daisy Roots
turn-up trousers, and I call them Round the Houses
a ragged shirt, and I call it Dicky Dirt
an old top hat, and I call it Tit-for-Tat
straw for my hair, and I call it Barnet Fair . . .

Add as many clothes as you can think
of for Uncle Joe, giving them names
in rhyming slang. Can you make
scarecrow music with scrapes, rattles
and scrunchy sounds?

Cockles and mussels

1 In Dub-lin's fair ci - ty, Where the girls are so pret-ty, I

first set my eyes on sweet Mol - ly Ma - lone, As she

wheeled her wheel - bar-row Through streets broad and nar-row, Cry-ing

'Cock-les and Mus-sels! A - live, a - live - o!' 'A -

live, a - live - o,___ a - live, a - live - o,'___ Cry-ing

'Cock - les and Mus-sels! A - live, a - live o!'

Another firm-favourite. See if you can build up the list of sea-food, in each chorus, eg 'Cockles and mussels, and oysters, and winkles, and whelks! Alive, alive-o!'

1 In Dublin's fair city, where the girls are so pretty,
I first set my eyes on sweet Molly Malone,
As she wheeled her wheel-barrow
Through streets broad and narrow,
Crying 'Cockles and Mussels! Alive, alive-o!'

Chorus:
Alive, alive-o, Alive, alive-o,
Crying 'Cockles and Mussels! Alive, alive-o!'

2 She was a fishmonger, but sure 'twas no wonder,
For so were her father and mother before.
And they each wheeled their barrow
Through streets broad and narrow,
Crying 'Cockles and Mussels! Alive, alive-o!'

Chorus

3 She died of a fever and no one could save her,
And that was the end of sweet Molly Malone.
But her ghost wheels her barrow
Through streets broad and narrow,
Crying 'Cockles and Mussels! Alive, alive-o!'

Chorus

53

My Aunt Jane

Traditional Irish

1 My Aunt Jane, she called me in,
She gave me tea out of her wee tin.
Half a bap with a wee snow top
Three black lumps out of her wee shop.

2 My Aunt Jane she's awful smart
She bakes wee rings in an apple tart
And when Hallow eve comes round
Near that tart I'm always found.

3 My Aunt Jane has a bell at the door
A white stone step and a clean swept floor
Candy apples, hard green pears,
Conversation lozenges.

4 My Aunt Jane, she called me in,
She gave me tea out of her wee tin.
Half a bap with a wee snow top
Three black lumps out of her wee shop.

Do you have a bell at your front door? Can you sing the tune the chimes make? Have a go at making up a new chime-tune using just four notes on glockenspiel or chime-bars.

What other sounds are used to sell sweet things? Ice-cream van-chimes? Advertising jingles? Can you remember how some of these sound?

With some friends, you could make a wall-picture of a parade of shops, each one having its own special front-door, with all kinds of things in the window.

Ask your dentist about eating sweets!

Pease pudding hot

Traditional English

1 Pease pudding hot!
Pease pudding cold!
Pease pudding in the pot,
Nine days old.

2 Some like it hot,
Some like it cold,
Some like it in the pot,
Nine days old.

How do *you* like it?

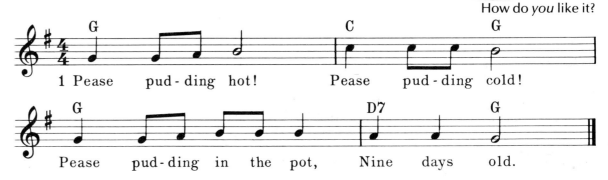

Lazy Mary

Traditional English, adapted Alison McMorland

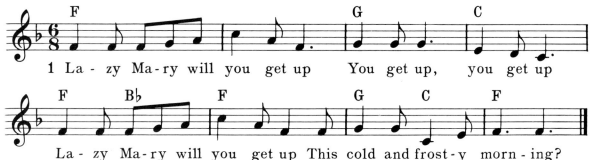

1 La - zy Ma-ry will you get up   You get up,   you get up

La - zy Ma-ry will you get up This cold and frost-y morn - ing?

Hot Cross Buns

Traditional English

Hot Cross Buns!   Hot Cross Buns!   One a pen-ny, two a pen-ny,

Hot Cross Buns!   If you have no daugh-ters, give them to your sons,

One a pen - ny, two a pen - ny, Hot Cross Buns!

Hot Cross Buns!
Hot Cross Buns!
One a penny, two a penny,
Hot Cross Buns!
If you have no daughters,
Give them to your sons,
One a penny, two a penny,
Hot Cross Buns!

1 Lazy Mary, will you get up,
  You get up, you get up,
  Lazy Mary, will you get up,
  This cold and frosty morning?

2 No, Mother, I won't get up,
  Won't get up, won't get up.
  No, Mother, I won't get up
  This cold and frosty morning.

3 What if I give you some toast and honey,
  Toast and honey, toast and honey?
  What if I give you some toast and honey
  This cold and frosty morning?

4 No, Mother, I won't get up,
  Won't get up, won't get up.
  No, Mother, I won't get up
  This cold and frosty morning.

5 What if I give you some strawberry ice-cream,
  Strawberry ice-cream, strawberry ice-cream?
  What if I give you some strawberry ice-cream
  This cold and frosty morning?

6 No, Mother, I won't get up,
  Won't get up, won't get up.
  No, Mother, I won't get up
  This cold and frosty morning.

7 What if I give you *. .
  . . . .
  What if I give you . . . .
  This cold and frosty morning?

8 Yes, Mother, I will get up,
  Will get up, will get up.
  Yes, Mother, I will get up
  This cold and frosty morning.

* *Insert* your *favourite food.*

55

Coconut woman

Words: Harry Belafonte   Music: Lord Burgess

1 Co-co-nut wo-man is call-ing out And ev-'ry day you can hear her shout. Co-co-nut wo-man is call-ing out And ev-'ry day you can hear her shout 'Get your co-co-nut wa-ter, *four for five!* Man it's good for your daugh-ter, *four for five!* Co-co got-ta lot-ta i-ron, *four for five!* Make you strong like a li-on, *four for five!*

2 A lady tell me the other day,
No one can take her sweet man away.
I ask her what was the mystery?
She say coconut water and rice curry.
You can cook it in a pot, *four for five,*
You can serve it very hot, *four for five,*
Coco gotta lotta iron, *four for five,*
Make you strong like a lion, *four for five.*

3 Coconut woman say you'll agree
Coconut make very nice candy,
The thing that's best if you're feeling glum
Is coconut water with a little rum.
It could make you very tipsy, *four for five,*
Make you feel very frisky, *four for five,*
Coco gotta lotta iron, *four for five,*
Make you strong like a lion, *four for five.*

Wind blows Mangoes

Traditional Bengali

Chorus

Wind blows, wind blows, Drop, drop man-goes, Green and_ ripe ones,

Sweet and sour__ Oh no! Here comes a pour-ing

shower. Here comes a pour-ing shower. *Verse* Drop, drop man-goes

in the front and the back, Quick, quick, pick them, put them in the sack!

Hur-ry up_ let's go, here's my hand to hold. We'll_ all_ get soaked,

we will catch a nas-ty cold. No_ more hap-py hours. Oh no!

Here come pour-ing showers. Here come pour-ing showers.

The herring's head

1 What'll we do with the herring's *head*,
Oh, what'll we do with the herring's *head*?
We'll make it into loaves of bread.
Herring's *head*, loaves of bread,
And all sorts of things.

Chorus:
Of all the fish that live in the sea,
The herring is the fish for me,
Sing fa-la-la li-do,
Fa-la-la li-do li-day.
Fa-la-la li-do, fa-la-la li-do li-day.

2 What'll we do with the herring's *eyes*,
Oh, what'll we do with the herring's *eyes*?
We'll make them into puddings and pies;
Herring's *eyes*, puddings and pies;
Herring's *head*, loaves of bread,
And all sorts of things.

Chorus

Each new verse gets longer by adding a new object at the top of your list:

3 . . . herring's *fins* . . . needles and pins.

Chorus

4 . . . herring's *belly* . . . a lass called Nelly.

Chorus

5 . . . herring's *tail* . . . a ship that sails.

* *Repeat as necessary*

You can add actions by touching your head, eyes, back and belly at the right places in the song, gradually building up the list. Waggling hands can make fins and a tail!

Can you make fishy music with water-bubbles (straw in a glass), blowing instruments, swishing cymbals and chime-bars?

Magical food

Words and Music: Malvina Reynolds, adapted Barry Gibson

Take a bite of mystical, magical food, it's good.

1 Take a bite of carrot, you'll become a parrot.
Take a bite of cheese, you'll be a Pekinese.
Take a bite of toast, you'll become a ghost.
Take a bite of mystical, magical food, it's good.

2 Take a bite of cake, you'll become a snake.
Take a bite of tea, you'll become a bee.
Take some macaroni, you'll become a pony.
Take a bite of mystical, magical food, it's good.

3 Take a bite of fruit, you'll become a newt.
Take a bite of pear, you'll become a bear.
Take a bite of prune, you'll jump across the moon.
Take a bite of mystical, magical food, it's good.

4 Take a bite of spud, you'll be a pool of mud.
Take a bite of onion, you'll become a bunion,
Take a sip of juice, you'll become a moose.
Take a bite of mystical, magical food, it's good.

5 Take a bite of fun, grow food for everyone.
So take a seed and sow, and watch the magic grow.
For bags of food to spare, it's simple – we just share!
Take a bite of mystical, magical food, it's good.

Make up some words about *your* favourite foods.

The whiting

This song can work well as a fishing game. The 'fishers' hold hands in a circle, and dance to the left (line 1), then the right (line 2). From line 3, they clap (on the spot) for every 'whiting' and re-join hands for every 'too-re-lah'.

In the middle are a 'sun-fish' and a 'whiting', who try to escape from the 'net' during the 'whiting' claps. If they get out, they can choose someone to become their kind of fish. The first fish-team to reach a chosen number wins.

The sun-fish is a mighty fish to all the Galway fishermen,
But whiting is far finer and bound to satisfy them,
O whiting too-re-lah and whiting too-re-laddie-o.
Whiting too-re-lah and whiting too-re-laddie,
O whiting too-re-lah, O the whiting is the fish for me,
O whiting too-re-lah, and whiting too-re-laddie-o.

Say, bonnie lassie

Say, bon-nie las-sie, Will you gang with me to the bon-nie, bon-nie house of Aa-ron? Say bon-nie las-sie, Will you gang with me to__ feed my fa-ther's ducks? With a quack, quack here and a quack, quack there, Here a quack, there a quack, ev-'ry-where a quack, quack, Hey bon-nie las-sie, Will you gang with me to the bon-nie bon-nie house of Aa-ron?

Say, bonnie lassie,
Will you gang* with me to the bonnie bonnie house of Aaron?
Say, bonnie lassie,
Will you gang with me to feed my father's ducks?
With a quack, quack here and a quack, quack there,
Here a quack, there a quack, everywhere a quack, quack,
Say, bonnie lassie,
Will you gang with me to the bonnie bonnie house of Aaron?

* = go

A good alternative to Old MacDonald, with a lovely tune. After 'my father's ducks', sing verses for the chickens (*with a cluck cluck here*), sheep (*and a baa baa there*), and cows (*everywhere a moo moo*) in our picture. Then try 'my father's cats' (*miaow miaow*), 'my father's armadillos' (*? ?*) and 'my father's gnus (*gnu gnu?*).

Mama lend me your pigeon

Traditional West Indian

1 Ma-ma lend me your pig-eon, to keep comp'ny with mine.

Ma-ma lend me your pig-eon to keep comp'ny with mine.

My pig-eon gone wild in the bush, my pig-eon gone wild.

My pig-eon gone wild in the bush, my pig-eon gone wild.

1 Mama lend me your pigeon to keep comp'ny with mine,
Mama lend me your pigeon to keep comp'ny with mine,
My pigeon gone wild in the bush, my pigeon gone wild,
My pigeon gone wild in the bush, my pigeon gone wild.

2 Mama lend me your turtle to keep comp'ny with mine,
Mama lend me your turtle to keep comp'ny with mine,
My turtle gone swim in the pond, my turtle gone wild,
My turtle gone swim in the pond, my turtle gone wild.

3 Mama lend me your rooster to keep comp'ny with mine,
Mama lend me your rooster to keep comp'ny with mine,
My rooster gone 'quack, quack, quack', my rooster gone wild,
My rooster gone 'quack, quack, quack', my rooster gone wild.

4 Mama lend me your hippo to keep comp'ny with mine,
Mama lend me your hippo to keep comp'ny with mine,
My hippo gone swing in the trees, my hippo gone wild,
My hippo gone swing in the trees, my hippo gone wild.

5 Mama lend me your leopard to keep comp'ny with mine,
Mama lend me your leopard to keep comp'ny with mine,
My leopard gone laze in the daisies, my leopard gone wild,
My leopard gone laze in the daisies, my leopard gone wild.

6 Mama lend me your penguin to keep comp'ny with mine,
Mama lend me your penguin to keep comp'ny with mine,
My penguin gone slide in the ice, my penguin gone wild,
My penguin gone slide in the ice, my penguin gone wild.

Hoist the window

Chorus

C
Hoist the win - dow, hoist the win - dow, F7

Let the dove come in. G6 C

Verse
C
1 When that dove went a - way

am G6 C
Well it rained most ev - er - y day.

There was storm there was tem - pest

am G6 C
All the child - ren start to cry.

Chorus:
Hoist the window, hoist the window,
Let the dove come in.
Hoist the window, hoist the window,
Let the dove come in.

1 When that dove went away,
Well it rained most every day.
There was storm, there was tempest,
All the children start to cry.

Chorus

2 But when that dove flew this way,
Well the sun came out to stay.
All the children sang together
And the dry bones lived again.

Chorus

◀ Can you make flapping shapes with your hands for
pigeons, doves, roosters (cockerels), and penguins?
These can look really good in silhouette, if you use a
spotlight or torch in a dark room. And why not make a
turtle, a hippo and a leopard from clay?

The bird song

1 'Hi!' says the blackbird, sitting on a chair,
  'Once I courted a lady fair;
  She proved fickle and turned her back
  And ever since then I've dressed in black'.

2 'Hi!' says the blue-jay as she flew,
  'If I was a young man, I'd have two.
  If one proved fickle and chanced to go,
  I'd have a new string to my bow'.

3 'Hi!' says the little leather-winged bat,
  'I will tell you the reason that,
  The reason that I fly at night
  Is because I lost my heart's delight'.

4 'Hi!' says the little mourning dove,
  'I'll tell you how to gain her love,
  Court her night and court her day,
  Never give her time to say "Oh, nay!"'

5 'Hi!' says the robin, with a little squirm,
  'I wish I had a great big worm;
  I'd fly away into my nest;
  I have a wife I think is best'.

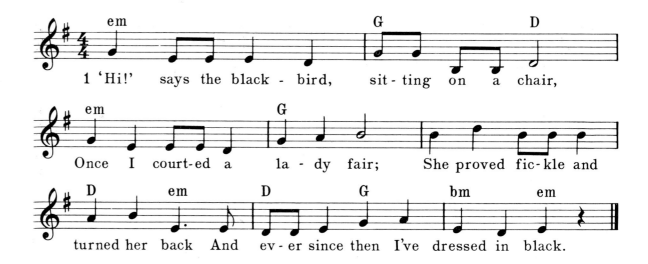

Can birds talk? How do they send messages? Listen to birdsong, coming from bushes, trees and gardens, or from recordings. With a friend, you could make up some bird-conversations, using whistling instead of words. Then try making bird-sounds with recorders, different kinds of whistles, or 'nightingale' warblers (you fill these up with water). Swanee whistles can make good cooing sounds just like a dove. Coo!

The snow-white bird

Traditional Netherlands

1 There was a lit - tle snow-white bird,
There was a lit - tle snow-white bird, All on a
prick-ly thorn was perched, Der - ry down_ down,
All on a prick-ly thorn was perched, Der-ry down.

1 There was a little snow-white bird,
There was a little snow-white bird,
All on a prickly thorn was perched,
Derry down down,
All on a prickly thorn was perched,
Derry down.

2 O nightingale, oh little bird,
O nightingale, oh little bird,
Oh will you be my messenger?
Derry down down,
Oh will you be my messenger?
Derry down.

3 How can I be your messenger,
How can I be your messenger,
When I am but a tiny bird?
Derry down down,
When I am but a tiny bird?
Derry down.

4 Although you're small you're swift of wing,
Although you're small you're swift of wing,
This letter to my true love bring.
Derry down down,
This letter to my true love bring,
Derry down.

5 He took the letter in his beak,
He took the letter in his beak,
And flew among the dark, green trees.
Derry down down,
And flew among the dark, green trees.
Derry down.

A soft, gentle song, to be sung very, very quietly. This sounds lovely with a simple drone (the note G) played continuously on any string or percussion instruments. Can you make a snow-white bird from folded paper?

65

Kookaburra

Kookaburra sits on an old gum tree,
Merry, merry king of the bush is he,
Laugh, kookaburra, laugh, kookaburra,
Gay your life must be.

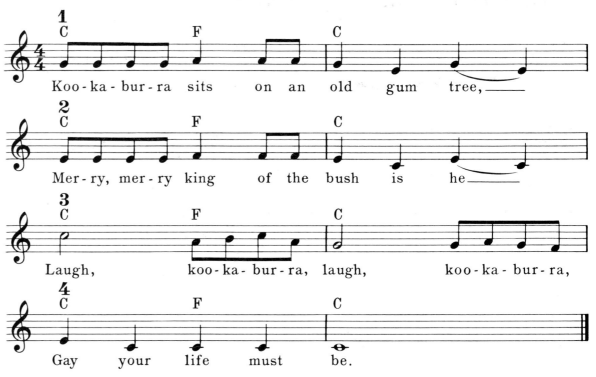

1
C ... F ... C
Koo - ka - bur - ra sits on an old gum tree, ——

2
C ... F ... C
Mer - ry, mer - ry king of the bush is he ——

3
C ... F ... C
Laugh, koo - ka - bur - ra, laugh, koo - ka - bur - ra,

4
C ... F ... C
Gay your life must be.

Kookaburra is a *round*, which means that several people can sing it in 'parts'. One person (or group) starts, and another begins only when they reach number 2. You can eventually build up to four parts by 'staggering' the start points (1-2-3-4). You could make up verses about other birds, eg:
    'Song thrush sitting on the garden gate . . .'
        or
    'Parrot sitting on the pet shop perch . . .'

Pretty pussy purr

Traditional British

(Prrrrrrrr) (Prrrrrrrrr) (Prrrrrrrrr) (Prrrrrrrrr)

1 Pret-ty puss-y purr, Where did you lose your fur?

On the way to Fish-guard, And the wind was bit-ter, Sir.

2 Prrrrrrr, Prrrrrrr, Prrrrrrr, Prrrrrrr,
Tell me, pussy sweet,
What did you have to eat?
Halibut and custard
And it was a real treat.

3 Prrrrrrr, Prrrrrrr, Prrrrrrr, Prrrrrrr,
Listen, pussy dear,
You mustn't stray from here,
But I enjoy my journeys –
I'm a cat that knows no fear.

What is your cat's favourite food?

Little green frog

Traditional Turkish

(Chorus same tune)

1 Lit-tle green frog, lit-tle green frog, Where's your tail so small? I

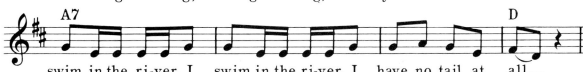

swim in the ri-ver, I swim in the ri-ver, I have no tail at all. _

Can you make froggy sounds with your voice,
or a home-made scraper?

Chorus

2 Little green frog, little green frog,
Where's your wing so small?
I swim in the river, I swim in the river,
I have no wing at all.

Koo wak wak wak, koo wak wak wak
Koo wak wak wak wak wak
Koo wak wak wak, koo wak wak wak
Koo wak wak wak wak wak.

3 Little green frog, little green frog,
Where's your house so small?
I swim in the river, I swim in the river,
I have no house at all. *Chorus*

When I was a hedgehog

Words: Traditional English, adapted Barry Gibson
Music: Traditional Austrian

1 When I was a *hedgehog*, a *hedgehog*, a *hedgehog*,
When I was a *hedgehog*, a *hedgehog* was I.
It was this way, and that way,
And this way, and that way,
When I was a *hedgehog*, a *hedgehog* was I.

2 When I was a *kitten* . . .

3 When I was a *blackbird* . . .

4 When I was a *cuckoo* . . .

5 When I was an *ostrich* . . .

6 When I was a *herring* . . .

7 When I was a *parrot* . . .

This well-known tune makes a good circle-dance. Dance to the left for one verse, right for the next, and so on. On every 'this way' and 'that way' stay where you are and mime the silliest actions you can think of for each animal.

1 When I___ was a hedge-hog, a hedge-hog, a
hedge-hog, When I___ was a hedge-hog, a hedge-hog was
I. It was this way, and that way, and this way, and
that way, When I___ was a hedge-hog, a hedge-hog was I.

Kangaroos like to hop

Words and Music: Leon Rosselson

1 Kan-ga-roos like to hop,___ And Ze-bras like to run,___

Hor-ses like to trot,___ But I like to lie in the sun.

For this one, you can collect together lots of instruments, sound-makers or noisy toys to make all the sounds at the end of each line (*boing, trot, dring dring, glug, splash, . . .*). If you run out of sounds, just do some actions!

1 Kangaroos like to hop,
And zebras like to run,
Horses like to trot,
But I like to lie in the sun.

2 Hooters like to hoot,
And bells like to ring,
Scooters like to scoot,
But I like to swing on a swing.

3 Water likes to trickle,
And milk likes to spill,
Glue likes to stickle,
But I like to roll down the hill.

4 Creepers like to creep,
And winkles like to wink,
People like to peep,
But I like to splash in the sink.

5 Panthers like to growl,
And leopards like to leap,
Wolves like to howl,
But I like to sing in my sleep.

6 Kangaroos like to hop,
And zebras like to run,
Horses like to trot,
But I like to lie in the sun.

Old Blue

1 I had an old dog, boys,__ and I called him Blue,
Lis-ten, let me tell you what Blue could do.

Chorus
Come on, Blue,__ __ you good dog, you. Yes,__ come on, Blue,__ you good dog you.

2 I took my axe, boys, and I blowed my horn,
Going a-hunting as sure as you're born.

Chorus

3 Old Blue treed and I went to see,
Had him a possum up a white oak tree.

Chorus

4 He growled at me, I looked at him,
I shook him out, Blue took him in.

Chorus

5 Baked that possum good and brown,
Laid the sweet 'taters round and round.

Final Chorus:
Say, come on, Blue, you can have some, too.
Yes, come on, Blue, you can have some, too.

A grisly story for the poor old possum! What do you think about hunting? Have you ever heard a horn? You can make sounds a bit like a hunting horn by blowing raspberries down a hosepipe with a funnel at the end. Try it!

70

The squirrel

Traditional Danish

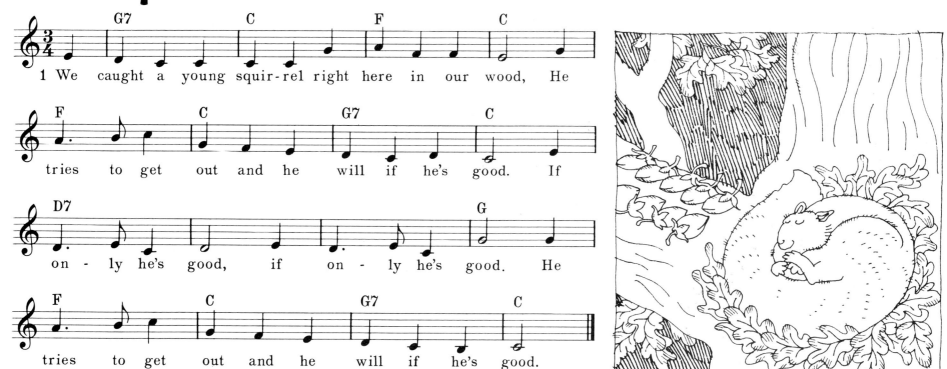

1 We caught a young squir-rel right here in our wood, He tries to get out and he will if he's good. If on-ly he's good, if on-ly he's good. He tries to get out and he will if he's good.

2 The wind it was shaking the nuts from the trees!
One dropped on his nose and it made squirrel sneeze.
It made squirrel sneeze, it made squirrel sneeze.
One dropped on his nose and it made squirrel sneeze.

3 He picked them all up – yes he did – with his toes,
And laid them in order in beautiful rows.
In beautiful rows, in beautiful rows,
And laid them in order in beautiful rows.

4 He knelt in the grass and he made him a nest.
He ate all the nuts and sat down for a rest.
Sat down for a rest, sat down for a rest.
He ate all the nuts and sat down for a rest.

5 He dropped off to sleep on that warm afternoon,
And he slept on and on till the middle of June!
The middle of June, the middle of June,
And he slept on and on till the middle of June!

Try actions for these things in the song:
shake the tree – touch your nose – sneeze – pick up with toes – lay in rows – kneel to make nest – rest head on hands – lie down and snooze!

Katie Bairdie

Can you dance in time to *Katie Bairdie*? Make up verses for other animals you think she had. And for *Me Grandfather Died* try to make new verses with a short story which rhymes.

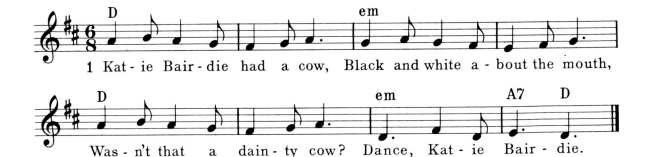

1 Kat - ie Bair - die had a cow, Black and white a - bout the mouth,
Was - n't that a dain - ty cow? Dance, Kat - ie Bair - die.

2 Katie Bairdie had a cat,
She could catch a mouse or rat,
Wasn't that a dainty cat?
Dance, Katie Bairdie.

3 Katie Bairdie had a hen
She could lay both but and ben*
Wasn't that a dainty hen?
Dance, Katie Bairdie.

4 Katie Bairdie had a grice†,
He could skate upon the ice,
Wasn't that a dainty grice?
Dance, Katie Bairdie.

5 Katie Bairdie had a wean‡
Wouldn't play out in the rain,
Wasn't that a dainty wean?
Dance, Katie Bairdie.

* = in and out   † = a little pig
‡ = a child

Me grandfather died

1 Me grand-fa-ther died and he left me a mule, A

sil-ly old mule and he fol-lowed me to school. *And it's*

ee - aye - ad - dy - o, Mam-my and your dad-dy - o,

Ee - aye - ad - dy o, Down by the Lu - can dair - y.

1 Me grandfather died and he left me a mule,
A silly old mule and he followed me to school.

Chorus

2 Me grandfather died and he left me a pig,
A fat little pig and he danced me a jig.

Chorus

3 Me grandfather died and he left me a hen,
A fat little hen and she laid now and then.

Chorus

4 Me grandfather died and he left me a drake,
A fat little drake, he was swallowed by a snake.

Chorus

One more river

1 Old No-ah once he built an ark, *There's one more ri-ver to cross,* He patched it up with hick-o-ry bark, *There's one more ri-ver to cross.* One more ri-ver,— and that's the ri-ver of Jor-dan, One more ri-ver,— and that's the ri-ver to cross.

2 The animals went in one by one . . .
The elephant chewed a currant bun.

3 The animals went in two by two . . .
Rhinoceros and kangaroo.

4 The animals went in three by three . . .
The bear, the flea, the bumble-bee.

5 The animals went in four by four . . .
Old Noah got mad and hollered for more.

6 The animals went in five by five . . .
The bees mistook the bear for a hive.

7 The animals went in six by six . . .
The hyena laughed at the monkey's tricks.

There was a pig

(oink, oink, oink, oink) There was a pig went out to dig,
Chris-si-mas Day, Chris-si-mas Day, There was a pig went out to dig, Chri-si-mas Day in the morn - ing.

2 There was a cow went out to plough . . .

3 There was a sparrow went out to harrow . . .

4 There was a drake went out to rake . . .

5 There was a crow went out to sow . . .

6 There was a sheep went out to reap . . .

Both these songs can be as long as you want to make them. Just add all the animals which you can make rhyme. And the more animal actions, the merrier. . .

Get about

Words and Music: Barry Gibson

The action part of the song (marked *) is optional, for when you're in a large space. If you like, take longer to do the actions than the music says. Here are some suggestions:

Tractor (*turn huge steering wheel*), van (*pull starter*), bicycle (*ring bell*), charabanc (*jog up and down*), dinghy (*swish side-to-side*), balloon (*hand sails away*), spaceship (*make 2-hand rocket*), moon (*2-hand circle*), trainers (*run on the spot*), street (*turn on the spot*), traffic (*look right-left-right*), feet (*clump feet*).

Then try verses and actions about *your* favourite ways of getting about, eg railway, roller-skates, car, digger, pony, hovercraft. . . .

1 Get about on a tractor,
Get about in a van.
Get about on a bicycle,
Or old charabanc.
Get about, get about if you can!

2 Get about in a dinghy,
Get about in a balloon,
Get about in a spaceship,
Flying up to the moon.
Get about, get about very soon.

3 Get about in your trainers,
Get about in your street,
But watch out for the traffic,
Don't fall over you feet.
Get about, make your journey complete!

Riding in my car

Words and Music: Woody Guthrie

Guitar Tab

Chorus:
Take you riding in my car, car
Take you riding in my car, car
Take you riding in my car, car
Take you riding in my car.

1 Click clack, open up a door, girls
  Click clack, open up a door, boys
  Front door, back door, clickety clack
  Take you riding in my car.

  Chorus

2 Climb, climb on a front seat
  Spree I spraddle on a back seat
  Turn my key, step on my starter
  Take you riding in my car.

  Chorus

3 I'm going to let you blow the horn
  I'm going to let you blow the horn
  Oorah oorahh oogah oogahh
  Take you riding in my car.

  Chorus

4 I'm going to roll you home again
  I'm going to roll you home again
  Brrm brrm chrrka chrrka rolly home
  Take you riding in my car.

  Chorus

It might be wise to give your children a cautionary word about cars and strangers.

Zum gali gali

Words: Anne Mendoza
Music: Traditional Israeli

Chorus:
Zum gali gali now the wheel is a-turning
Zum gali gali now the wheel is a-turning
Zum gali gali now the wheel is a-turning
Zum gali gali now the wheel is a-turning

1 Let us sing with joy as we work
  Let us work with joy as we sing
  Let us sing with joy as we work
  Let us work with joy as we sing.

Chorus:

2 Let us work for peace in the world
  For in peace we can sing as we work.
  Let us work for peace in the world
  For in peace we can sing as we work.

Chorus

Add verses for special kinds of work or actions you can do *together*, eg:
      Let us plant our seeds in the ground . . .
        or
      Let us build a new house today . . .
        or
      Let us turn right round, where we are . . .
        or
      Let us reach right up to the sky . . .

This makes a good circle dance. Holding hands, all step to the left for the first half of the chorus, then back to the right. In the verses, all bring your hands to the centre (lines 1 and 3) and back out to the ring (lines 2–4), or do the actions for your new verses.

Roll the old chariot

Traditional North American, adapted Barry Gibson

1 A big ice-cream would-n't do us a-ny harm, A

big ice-cream would-n't do us a-ny harm, A

big ice-cream would-n't do us a-ny harm And we'll

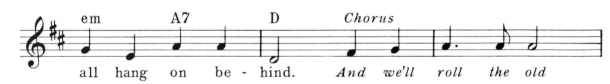

all hang on be-hind. *And we'll roll the old*

cha-ri-ot a-long, Roll the old cha-ri-ot a-long,

Roll the old cha-ri-ot a-long And we'll all hang on be-hind.

A non-government health-warning that ice-cream can damage your dental health, could lead to some fun verses about:

A visit to the dentist . . .

or

A brush of the teeth . . .

And an extra reminder about keeping safe when there's traffic around the back of ice-cream vans wouldn't do us any harm!

2 A ride to the sea
   wouldn't do us any harm . . .

Chorus

3 A train to the zoo
   wouldn't do us any harm . . .

Chorus

4 A bus to the fair
   wouldn't do us any harm . . .

Chorus

Roll that brown jug

Traditional North American, adapted Barry Gibson

When you've sung these verses about rolling, riding and walking, make up more verses with other ways of getting something somewhere. How about *whizz, heave* or *blow*? And can you make the somethings have nice bright colours, like orange, purple or yellow?

1 Roll that brown jug down to town, Roll that brown jug down to town,

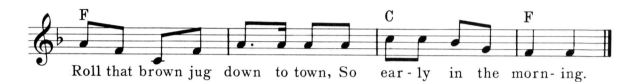

Roll that brown jug down to town, So ear-ly in the morn-ing.

1 Roll that brown jug down to town
Roll that brown jug down to town
Roll that brown jug down to town
So early in the morning.

2 Ride that red bike down to town
Ride that red bike down to town
Ride that red bike down to town
So early in the morning.

3 Walk that blue dog home again
Walk that blue dog home again
Walk that blue dog home again
So early in the morning.

4 Roll your green self down to school
Roll your green self down to school
Roll your green self down to school
So early in the morning.

Going to Boston

Traditional North American

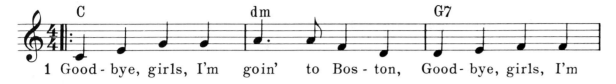

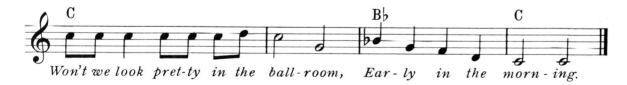

1 Good-bye, girls, I'm goin' to Boston
Good-bye, girls, I'm goin' to Boston
Good-bye, girls, I'm goin' to Boston
Early in the morning.

Chorus:
Won't we look pretty in the ballroom
Won't we look pretty in the ballroom
Won't we look pretty in the ballroom
Early in the morning.

2 Out of the way, you'll get run over, (*three times*)
Early in the morning
Rights and lefts to make it better, (*three times*)
Early in the morning.

Chorus

3 Swing your partner all the way to Boston,
(*three times*)
Early in the morning
Johnny, Johnny, gonna tell your pappy,
(*three times*)
Early in the morning.

Chorus

Song of the Delhi Tongawallah

Traditional Hindustani

1 Gallop quickly, gallop quickly,
  Gallop quickly brother horse.
  Gallop quickly, gallop quickly
  Gallop quickly brother horse.

Chorus:
We have still five miles of trav'ling
And the shades of night are falling.
We have still five miles of trav'ling
And the shades of night are falling.

2 Grain and grass be yours in plenty
  If we get home quickly, horse.
  Grain and grass be yours in plenty
  If we get home quickly, horse.

Chorus

A song that you can try at different speeds, especially if
you make up verses, such as: 'Trot along gently . . .', or
'Walk so slowly . . .', or 'Take a rest now . . .', or 'Now get
faster, faster, faster . . .'. And for actions to go with them
find a nice large space.

Sleigh Ride

Traditional Russian

Gal - lop - ing a - cross the plains, rac - ing in the moon - light,

Hoof-beats sound-ing o'er the snow and all the sleigh-bells ring - ing.

Hoof-beats sound-ing o'er the snow, oh lis - ten to the bells— Hey!

Galloping across the plains
Racing in the moonlight
Hoof-beats sounding o'er the snow
And all the sleigh-bells ringing
Hoof-beats sounding o'er the snow
Oh listen to the bells – Hey!

Guitar Tab

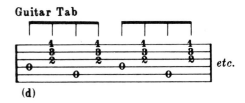

etc.

(d)

For percussion to go with this winter-time song, collect together as many jingling sounds as you can. As well as bells, you could try rattling coins, bunches of keys, bottle tops, buttons and foil on coat-hangers or in music-box shakers (see pages 8–9).

To make hoof-beat sounds for both songs, try coconut shells, yoghurt pots or woodblocks.

Sponge fishing

You can play a quiet bell sound, after the words 'ringing . . . bringing . . . singing . . . shore . . .'.

Bells are rung in different places on all kinds of occasions, at different times of day, and on special days of the year. How many kinds of bell have you heard? School bells? Church bells? Clock bells? Fire-engine bells? Telephone bells?

It's well worth looking out for some of the beautiful oriental bells which you can sometimes buy quite cheaply. These will add a real touch of magic to your music box. Indian and Chinese ones are often made from brass, while steel 'finger-cymbals' also have a long, ringing tone. Just listen together!

Little ship we'll go a-fishing
Out from the shore
Out from the shore
When the evening bell is ringing
Many sponges we'll be bringing
And we'll sail for home with singing
Out from the shore
Out from the shore.

When I'm on my journey

Traditional North American Spiritual

1 When I'm on my jour-ney don't you weep af-ter me___

When I'm on my jour-ney don't you weep af-ter me___

When I'm on my jour-ney don't you weep af-ter me___ I don't

last time

want you to weep af-ter me.

1 When I'm on my journey
Don't you weep after me
When I'm on my journey
Don't you weep after me
When I'm on my journey
Don't you weep after me
I don't want you to weep after me.

2 Every lonely river must
Go home to the sea
Every lonely river must
Go home to the sea
Every lonely river must
Go home to the sea
I don't want you to weep after me.

3 When the stars are falling
And the thunder starts to roll
When the stars are falling
And the thunder starts to roll
When the stars are falling
And the thunder starts to roll
I don't want you to weep after me.

4 High up on the mountain
Leave my sorrow down below
High up on the mountain
Leave my sorrow down below
High up on the mountain
Leave my sorrow down below
I don't want you to weep after me.

A good song for adding claps, finger-clicks, thigh-slaps and lots of good old gospel gusto. Afterwards, have a go at making music for stars falling (*bells, glockenspiel, chime-bars*) and thunder-rolling (*marbles in a big box, wobble-board made from a big sheet of hardboard*).

I have a little tiny house

Traditional Welsh
English Words: Mari Griffiths

2 I do no work, I sit and watch
    I sit and watch I sit and watch.
    I do no work, I sit and watch
    The high tide and the low tide.
    Hi-dee-do, de-hi-dee-hidee-ho,
    The high tide and the low tide.

3 And here I live and eat and sleep
    And eat and sleep and eat and sleep;
    And here I live and eat and sleep
    Contented by the fireside.
    Hi-dee-ho, de-hi-dee-hidee-ho,
    Contented by the fireside.

86

Gardens

Traditional Hebridean

Chorus

A day's work, a week's work As I go up and down,
There are man-y gar-dens All a-bout the town.

Verse

1 One that's gay with daff-o-dils, One where child-ren play,
One white with cher-ry flow'r, A-no-ther red with may.

2 A kitten and a lilac bush,
Bridal white and tall,
And later crimson roses
Against a granite wall.

Chorus

3 I have passed your railings
When you never knew,
And people who have gardens
I give my thanks to you.

Chorus

Tipsy topsy turvy town

Words: R. C. Scriven
Music: Michael Burnett

1 The cats and dogs walk upside down,
Daisies are black and buttercups brown,
The cows eat coal, the pigs eat hay,
In Tipsy-topsy-turvy-town.

2 The hens all swim, the ducks all drown,
Potatoes grow above the ground,
The clocks all go the wrong way round,
In Tipsy-topsy-turvy-town.

3 Cheese grows on trees and fires freeze,
And cats and kittens, if you please,
Eat salt-and-pepper sandwiches,
In Tipsy-topsy-turvy-town.

Hill an'gully

Hill an' Gul-ly ride - a, *Hill an' Gul-ly.*

Hill an' Gul-ly ride-a, *Hill an' Gul-ly.* An' a ben' dung low dung

Hill an' Gul-ly. An' a low dung bes-sy dung

Hill an' Gul-ly. An' yuh bet-ter min' yuh tum-ble dung *Hill an' Gul-ly.*

Hill an' Gully ride-a
Hill an' Gully.
Hill an' Gully ride-a
Hill an' Gully
An' a ben' dung low dung
Hill an' Gully
An' a low dung bessy dung
Hill an' Gully
An' yuh better min' yuh tumble dung
Hill an' Gully.

You can sing this in a pair, or in two groups, with one half singing just the refrain *'Hill an' Gully'*.

No accompaniment needed, except a few clicks or claps. Can you turn it into a clapping game?

The wreck

Words and Music: Jan Holdstock

1
em / B7
Un-der-neath the sea, Far a-way from land,

2
em / B7
That's where I will be, Shak-ing in the sand,

3
em / B7
Rat-tling in my rig-ging, Dith-'ring on my deck, I'm just a

4
em / B7
ner - - - - - vous wreck!

Underneath the sea,
  Far away from land,
That's where I will be,
  Shaking in the sand.
Rattling in my rigging,
  Dith'ring on my deck,
I'm just a nervous wreck!

Another song to try as a 'round' (see page 66), with several people joining in bit-by-bit. See pages 120–1 for ideas on how to add splashing, scraping, shaking and rattling sounds.

Guitar tablature

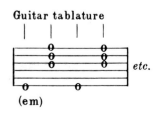

etc.

(em)

Widdecombe Fair

Traditional English

1 Tom Pearce, Tom Pearce,
   lend me thy grey mare,
   All along, down along, out along lea,
   For I want to go to Widdecombe Fair.

Chorus:
With Bill Brewer, Jan Stewer,
   Peter Gurney, Peter Davy,
Daniel Whiddon, Harry Hawk,
Old Uncle Tom Cobbleigh and all,
Old Uncle Tom Cobbleigh and all.

2 And when shall I see again my grey mare,
   All along, down along, out along lea,
   By Friday noon or Saturday soon,
   For I want to go to Widdecombe Fair.

Chorus

If you like, change the names in the chorus
to some of your friends' names.

The old steam radio

Words and Music: Barry Gibson

1 You can be a king or queen on a ma-gic dream ma-chine, On the old steam ra-di-o. You can jump a-cross the moon, you can e-ven stew a prune, On the old steam ra-di-o. You can burst a bag of fun, or a mould-y hot-cross bun, On the old steam ra-di-o. *The Old Steam Ra-di-o, my friends, The Old Steam Ra-di-o. Old Steam Ra-di-o.*

2 You can see amazing sights,
You can climb amazing heights, *on the Old Steam Radio.*
You can try and touch the sky,
You can ask the question 'Why?', *on the Old Steam Radio.*
Just take off those smelly socks,
And join in the Music Box, *on the Old Steam Radio.*

Chorus

3 There are scarecrows and green frogs,
There are hedgehogs and blue dogs, *on the Old Steam Radio.*
There are witches, there are lions,
There are Titches, There are Giants, *on the Old Steam Radio.*
There are super-duper dramas.
There are rotten blue bananas, *on the Old Steam Radio.*

Chorus

4 My Aunt Jane and Uncle Joe,
   Uncle Jack and Auntie Flo, *on the Old Steam Radio.*
   All the people you can meet
   On that busy, busy street! *on the Old Steam Radio.*
   If you follow it round the bend
   You may even make a friend! *on the Old Steam Radio.*

   Chorus

5 Well they sometimes make mistakes
   Like when Alfred burnt the cakes? *Oh the Old Steam Radio.*
   Did you hear that Tidy song
   Tied in knots, and all gone wrong? *Oh the Old Steam Radio.*
   Did you hear that kangaroo
   That hopped off to Timbuctoo? *Oh the Old Steam Radio.*

   Chorus

6 Why not prop it on a shelf
   And listen All by Yourself? *Oh the Old Steam Radio.*
   Ask a friend, or two, or many,
   Join and spin that Magic Penny, *oh the Old Steam Radio.*
   And then why not have a go –
   Make your own radio show? *Oh the Old Steam Radio.*

   Chorus

7 Well yours may not be hi-fi
   But it's always worth a try, *oh the Old Steam Radio.*
   Can you hear the voices mumble
   Through the crackles and the grumble? *Oh the Old Steam Radio.*
   If you can't, then count to ten,
   Twist the knob and Try Again! *Oh the Old Steam Radio.*

   Chorus

8 Well it may seem rather past it,
   Like a worn-out three-wheeled basket, *oh that Old Steam Radio.*
   But imagine, if you please,
   All the possibilities, *oh that Old Steam Radio.*
   So don't hang your head in sorrow
   'Cos it's coming back tomorrow, *oh that Old Steam Radio.*

   Chorus (twice)

Yes, why not have a go, make your own radio show
on tape?

So long

Words and Music: Woody Guthrie

1 I'll sing you a song, and I'll sing it__ a-gain, Of the place that I lived on, the dry wind-y plain, In the month of A-pril, in the coun-try called Clay, And here's what all of the peo-ple there say, they said:

Chorus
So long, it's been good to know you, So long, it's been good to know you, So long, it's been good to know you, This dust-y old dust is a-get-tin'_ my home, And I've got to be drift-ing a - long.__

2 That dust storm hit, and it hit like thunder
It dusted us over and covered us under
It blocked off the traffic and covered the sun
And straight for home all the people did run, singing:

Chorus

3 The church was jammed, the church was packed
That dusty old dust storm, it blowed so black
The preacher could not read a word of his text
So he folded his specs and he took up collection, singing:

Chorus

The North Wind doth blow

Traditional English

The North wind doth blow,_ And we shall have snow, And

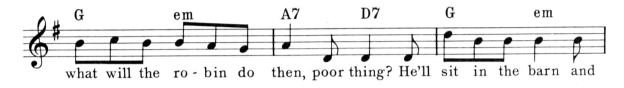

what will the ro-bin do then, poor thing? He'll sit in the barn and

keep him-self warm, And hide his head un-der his wing, poor thing.

The north wind doth blow,
And we shall have snow,
And what will the robin do then, poor thing?
He'll sit in the barn and keep himself warm,
And hide his head under his wing, poor thing.

A lovely, well-known tune. You can make up lots of verses about what different animals do when the cold winter wind blows. How about the badger . . ., or the squirrel . . ., or the rabbit . . ., or the chicken? And to make a song-story, add more verses about the pond . . ., and the scarecrow . . ., and the snowman . . .

Who has seen the wind?

Words: Christina Rossetti
Music: Jon Betmead

1 Who has seen the wind?
Neither I nor you,
But when the leaves hang trembling
The wind is passing through,
The wind is passing through.

2 Who has seen the wind?
Neither you nor I,
But when the trees bow down their heads
The wind is passing by,
The wind is passing by.

Have you seen the wind passing by? Listen to a tree near you to hear the wind passing through at different times of the year. Where else can you hear it huffing and puffing, hooting and whistling? Around buildings? Through doors? Near the sea?

If several people sing this song together, some of you could just make a quiet, windy background atmosphere . . . *whhhhoooo* . . . *shhhhhhh* . . .

Later, make up some windy music of your own with bottles, panpipes and other blowing instruments (see pages 7–9). Don't forget to have gentle shaking or rattling sounds for leaves trembling and some of the other things that the wind rustles or lifts in the air.

You could also make a collection of windy words, and invent some. Can you make them into a sort of poem?

Guitar tablature

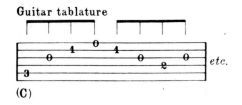

(C)

96

Weather song

Words and Music: Harriet Powell and John Wesley-Barker

Chorus

In all kinds of wea-ther, Whe-ther it's hot or cold
Would-n't it be nice if we could make the wea-ther do what it's told.

Verse

1 To make the sun Let's all hum _____ Hum, hum, hum Hum, hum, hum.

last time

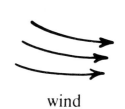
snow

clouds

Do you keep a weather diary? You can easily do this, just with pictures, drawing a different sign for each type of weather, either in a diary-book, or on a wall-chart.

wind

rain

Chorus:
In all kinds of weather,
Whether it's hot or cold,
Wouldn't it be nice if we could make
The weather do what it's told?

1 To make the sun
Let's all hum,
Hum, hum, hum,
Hum, hum, hum.

Chorus

2 To make the rain
Pat your knees,
Pat your knees,
Pat your knees.

Chorus

3 To make the wind
Let's all blow,
Blow, blow, blow,
Blow, blow, blow.

Chorus

You could copy the signs onto big cards and choose special sounds, for each one.

sun

FOG

Then, play these sounds in different orders to give a feeling of the weather changing, through the day, through the week, or through the year.

Where is the sun?

Words and Music: Leon Rosselson

Two songs which give a feeling of the darkness and the light in the changing year, as the seasons turn round.

Where is the Sun? is an evocative song with a haunting melody. You can hum it if you find the words tricky.

One-Two-Three makes a good circle-dance. Hold hands in a ring and dance to the left during the choruses. For the verses, why not make up some actions using your fingers, hands, whole body and, of course, eyes!

1 This winter land is a barren land And the walls are a wilderness high And hard and heavy is the wind And towers tear the sky. *The sun, the sun, oh where is the sun? The sky is cold as clay. And who is the devil who came from the dark And stole the sun away?*

1 This winter land is a barren land,
And the walls are a wilderness high,
And hard and heavy is the wind,
And towers tear the sky.

Chorus:
The sun, the sun, oh where is the sun?
The sky is cold as clay
And who is the devil
who came from the dark
And stole the sun away?

2 Once blackbirds sang in the trees and the grass,
And wild grew the rose,
Now no birds sing and the broken glass
Is all that ever grows.

Chorus

3 Of iron and stone the cage is made,
And golden is the key,
Iron and stone will never fade,
Oh who will set us free?

Chorus

One-two-three

Words and Music: Leon Rosselson

Chorus

E

1   2   3,   O-pen your eyes   and see,____   The

A   E   F♯   B7

sun has made the flow-ers grow for ev-'ry-one and me.   The

E

left   must take   the right,   All   a-round   the   ring,____   We've

A   E   [Choruses] F♯   B7

got   to   keep   the   cir-cle   mov-ing,   Ev-'ry-bo-dy   sing:

[Verses] F♯   B7

(the) wind   sets   it free.   *(Verses same tune)*

Chorus:
One-two-three, open your eyes and see,
The sun has made the flowers grow,
For everyone and me.
The left must take the right
All around the ring
We've got to keep the circle moving
Ev'rybody sing.

1 One-two-three, open your eyes and see,
The sun has made the flowers grow,
For everyone and me.
Out of the earth the root,
Out of the root, the tree,
The tree bears the fruit,
The wind sets it free.

Chorus

2 One-two-three, open your eyes and see,
The sun has made the flowers grow,
For everyone and me.
Out of the fruit, the seed,
Out of the seed, the root,
Out of the root, the tree,
The tree bears the fruit.

Last Chorus:
One-two-three, open your eyes and see,
Sky above and earth below,
For everyone and me.

Star flower

Words and Music: Malvina Reynolds

Have you ever looked at the shapes flowers make? There are lots that children can grow easily from seed, if you sow them in the spring. The easiest ones are 'annuals' and it's well worth trying Calendula (English marigold), Candytuft, Clarkia, Cornflower, Helichrysum (Straw-flower!), Larkspur, Linaria (Toadflax), Nigella (Love-in-a-mist), Stock and Viscaria.

Every time the word 'star' comes, you can add a quiet ringing sound on finger-cymbals, an Indian or Chinese bell, or a triangle.

1 Star flow-er O,   Star flow-er O,   Star flow-er in the ground O,

Who would e - ver know   such a flow-er O,   Would be shin-ing all a-

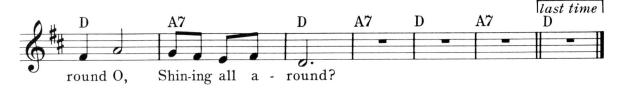

round O,   Shin-ing all a - round?

1 Star flower O,
Star flower O,
Star flower in the ground O,
Who would ever know such a flower O,
Would be shining all around O,
Shining all around?

2 Star flower O,
Star flower O,
Star flower by the reed O,
Who would ever know such a flower O,
Would be hiding in a seed O,
Hiding in a seed?

Guitar tablature

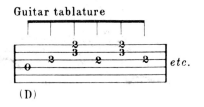

(D)

100

The Garden

Traditional English, adapted Barry Gibson

1 We sowed our gar-den full_ of seeds,—

We dug the soil, we pulled the weeds,—

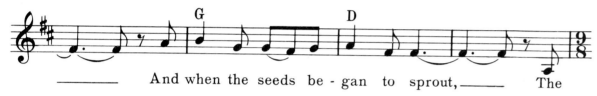

And when the seeds be-gan to sprout,— The

ti - ny leaves came pok - ing out.—

1 We sowed our garden full of seeds,
  We dug the soil, we pulled the weeds,
  And when the seeds began to sprout,
  The tiny leaves came poking out.

2 And then those leaves began to spread,
  They covered up our garden bed,
  And then the flowers began to bloom,
  We picked some for our living room.

3 And then those flowers they fell to the ground
  And then the snow (*shhh*) but not a sound (*pause*)
  And then the frost (*pause*) and then the rain (*shhhh*)
  And then the flowers came back again.

You could make hand actions or movements for each part of the song. Remember not to pick wild flowers: they need all the help they can get. Can you prepare a garden bed at your home or school?

The First of May

1 Soon will dawn the first of May, Mer - ry, mer - ri - ly ho - hay,

Soon will dawn the first of May, I will see my love to - day.

1 Soon will dawn the first of May,
Merry, merrily ho hay.
Soon will dawn the first of May,
I will see my love today.

2 To the greenwood I have gone,
Merry, merrily ho hay.
To the greenwood I have gone,
For my love to gather may.

3 As I plucked a branch of may,
Merry, merrily ho hay.
As I plucked a branch of may,
Merrily the drum did play.

4 As I carried back the may,
Merry, merrily ho hay,
As I carried back the may,
Merrily the fife did play.

5 Open love the door to me,
Merry, merrily ho hay.
Open love the door to me,
Here I bring a branch of may.

6 Soon will dawn the first of May,
Merry, merrily ho hay.
Soon will dawn the first of May,
I will see my love today.

The Rose Tree

Traditional

1 There is a tree in the garden gay.
   There is a tree in the garden gay.
   The flowers bloom in the month of May.
   The flowers bloom in the month of May.

2 Come pick a rose from that flow'ring tree.
   Come pick a rose from that flow'ring tree.
   And wear the rose as you dance with me.
   And wear the rose as you dance with me.

Both these songs work well with just a single drone note as accompaniment (G).

Treading the water wheel

Traditional Chinese
New words: Sandra Kerr

You could try this as a circle-dance, all holding hands and turning to the left (first half of each verse), then back to the right. For each *tap, tap*, stop briefly and touch your toes, feet, the ground, your nose, your elbow or whatever takes your fancy.

If you are just sitting, the *tap, tap* can also be played on any quiet tapping instrument (eg woodblock, temple-block, Chinese bell).

Have you ever had a chance to listen to the beautiful, delicate sound of Chinese instruments, either from recordings, or even better, live?

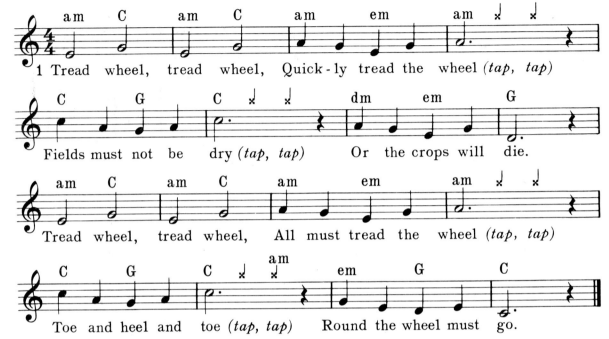

1 Tread wheel, tread wheel, Quick-ly tread the wheel *(tap, tap)*
Fields must not be dry *(tap, tap)* Or the crops will die.
Tread wheel, tread wheel, All must tread the wheel *(tap, tap)*
Toe and heel and toe *(tap, tap)* Round the wheel must go.

1 Tread wheel, tread wheel,
  Quickly, tread the wheel (*tap, tap*)
  Fields must not be dry (*tap, tap*)
  Or the crops will die.
  Tread wheel, tread wheel,
  All must tread the wheel (*tap, tap*)
  Toe and heel and toe (*tap, tap*)
  Round the wheel must go.

2 Tread wheel, tread wheel,
  Quickly, tread the wheel (*tap, tap*)
  Feet must never stop (*tap, tap*)
  Or we lose the crop.
  Tread wheel, tread wheel,
  All must tread the wheel (*tap, tap*)
  Work in every weather (*tap, tap*)
  Tread and turn together.

3 Tread wheel, tread wheel,
  Quickly, tread the wheel (*tap, tap*)
  Night turns into day (*tap, tap*)
  Still you'll hear us say
  Tread wheel, tread wheel,
  All must tread the wheel (*tap, tap*)
  Speed the wheel around (*tap, tap*)
  Feed the thirsty ground.

Guitar tablature

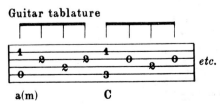

etc.

a(m)   C

Diwali

Words and Music: Niru Desai

Chorus:
Diwali is here, Diwali is here.
Happiness arrives, Happiness arrives.

1 Diwas lighted in every house
Rangoli patterns in every house.

Chorus

2 Decorations on every door
Tiny stars are shining bright.

Chorus

3 Crick, crack, crick, crack, crackers crack.
Mummy brings us lovely toys.

Chorus in Gujerati:
Diwali∗ avi, Diwali avi.
Anand lavi, anand lavi.

∗*Pronounced 'Div-ar-lee'.*

Diwali is the Hindu festival of lights. In late October, or early November, the skies in India become clear at the end of the harvest. The bright shining stars are seen as the beginning of the new year, when Rama leads the people from darkness to light.

A diva is a special kind of oil lamp to put on tables or windows. Look at different kinds of candle, and make Diwali flowers and door decorations for your room.

Rangoli is a floor pattern, at the entrance to a house or room, often made from cereals or pulses. Why not try making one?

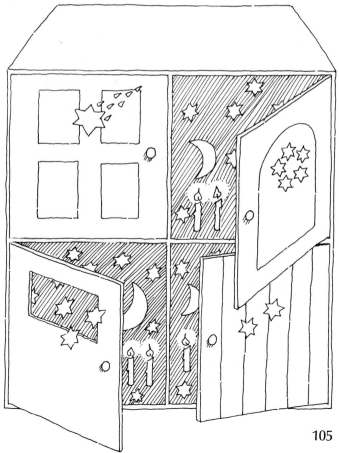

Mistletoe

Words and Music: John Perry

Two songs for the Christmas season. The actions here are fairly obvious! If anyone is too shy, they could always blow the kisses.

Chorus

Mis - tle - toe, mis - tle - toe, mis - tle mis - tle mis - tle - toe,

Adds to the Christ - mas cheer, First you kiss some -

bod - y, And wish them a Hap - py New Year.

Verse

1 First you kiss your hand, Kiss - es are for free,

Turn round to a friend, And put the kiss on their knee.

Chorus:
Mistletoe, mistletoe,
Mistle mistle mistletoe,
Adds to the Christmas cheer,
First you kiss somebody,
And wish them a Happy New Year.

1 First you kiss your hand,
Kisses are for free,
Turn round to a friend,
And put the kiss on their knee.

Chorus

2 First you kiss your hand,
You've got a kiss to spare,
Turn round to a friend,
And put the kiss on their hair.

Chorus

3 First you kiss your hand,
You don't have to speak – sh,
Turn round to a friend,
And put the kiss on their cheek.

Chorus

Sing Ivy

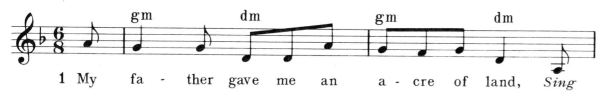

1 My fa - ther gave me an a - cre of land, Sing

o - vy, sing i - vy My fa - ther gave me an

a - cre of land, A bunch of green hol - ly and i - vy.

*Verse 9 only

With fif - ty bright gui - neas and an emp - ty sack,

The long story of this song is almost as mysterious as its magical plants, holly and ivy. If an adult can lead the singing, children will enjoy just joining in the beautiful refrain lines each time and following the images.

2 I harrowed it with a bramble bush . . .

3 I sowed it with two peppercorns . . .

4 I rolled it with a rolling pin . . .

5 I reaped it with my little penknife . . .

6 I stowed it in a mouse's hole . . .

7 I threshed it out with two bean stalks . . .

8 I sent my rats to the market with that . . .

9 My team of rats came rattling back
   Sing ovy, sing ivy
   My team of rats came rattling back
   With fifty bright guineas and an empty sack
   A bunch of green holly and ivy.

The Gower wassail

Traditional English

1 A wassail, a wassail throughout all this town,
   Our cup it is white and our ale it is brown.
   Our wassail is made of good ale and cake,
   Some nutmeg and ginger, the best we could get.

Chorus:
Fol the dol, fol the doldy dol,
Fol the doldy dol, fol the doldy dee,
Fol the dai rol, fol the day dee,
Sing too ral aye doh.

2 Our wassail is made of an elderberry bough,
   And so, my good neighbours,
      we'll drink unto thou
   Beside all on earth we have apples in store;
   Pray let us come in for 'tis cold by the door.

Chorus

3 We know by the moon that we are not too soon,
   And we know by the sky that we are not too high.
   We know by the stars that we are not too far
   And we know by the ground
      that we are within sound.

Chorus

Another song for the Christmas season. Explain the old British tradition of wassailing to children, and let them think of all the good things they like to smell and taste over Christmas. *'Let us come in'* (page 46) will make a good companion to this song.

108

Watch the stars

Traditional North American

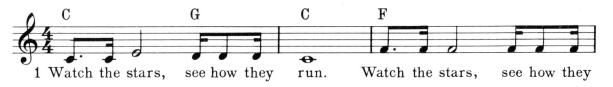

1 Watch the stars, see how they run,
   Watch the stars, see how they run,
   They all run down at the setting of the sun,
   Watch the stars, see how they run.

2 Watch the moon, see how it climbs,
   Watch the moon, see how it climbs,
   The moon climbs high at the sun setting time,
   Watch the moon, see how it climbs.

3 Watch the wind, see how it blows,
   Watch the wind, see how it blows,
   Well you ought to know that the wind's
       got to blow,
   Watch the wind, see how it blows.

4 Watch the clouds, see how they fly,
   Watch the clouds, see how they fly,
   They all run by on the windblown sky,
   Watch the clouds, see how they fly.

5 Watch the stars, see how they run,
   Watch the stars, see how they run,
   They all run down at the setting of the sun,
   Watch the stars, see how they run.

Can you make starry music (*bells, triangle, chimes*),
moony music (*xylophone, woodblocks*), windy music
(*blow*) and cloudy music (*paper rustles and sssssshhh*)?
Make star-shape mobiles for your room with card,
paper and foil, and cloud-shape ones from card or
polystyrene tiles:

Little nut tree

One of our best and most evocative nursery rhymes. The words mean just what you want them to mean. Can you make up sounds for the silver nutmeg (*shake a tambourine gently*) and the golden pear (*a soft tap on triangle or finger cymbals*)?

See if you can make the song's images into a story or short play. This could include a circle dance.

Guitar tablature

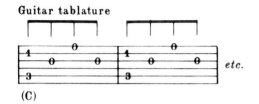

(C)

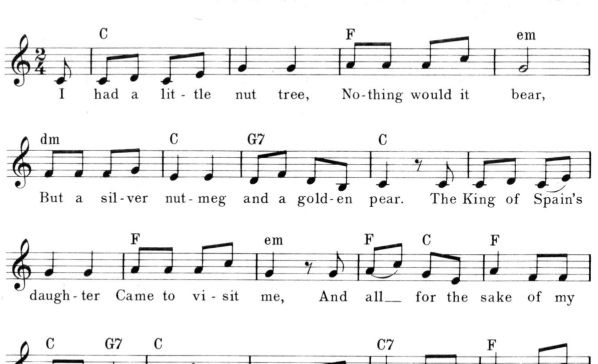

I had a lit-tle nut tree, No-thing would it bear, But a sil-ver nut-meg and a gold-en pear. The King of Spain's daugh-ter Came to vi-sit me, And all__ for the sake of my lit-tle nut tree. I skipped o-ver wa-ter, I danced o-ver sea, And all the birds in the air could-n't catch me.

I had a little nut tree, nothing would it bear,
But a silver nutmeg and a golden pear.
The King of Spain's daughter came to visit me,
And all for the sake of my little nut tree.
I skipped over water, I danced over sea,
And all the birds in the air couldn't catch me.

A Highland lullaby

1 I left my ba - by ly - ing there, Ly - ing
there, ly - ing there, I left my ba - by
ly - ing there To go and ga - ther blue - ber - ries.

A sad song with a beautiful, haunting melody, needing very little accompaniment (if any). Sing softly. Are you good at seeing signs of animals in quiet places? On a group walk or trip, see how many traces of animals you can see together, and how many animal sounds you can all hear. You'll need to be very, very quiet . . .

1 I left my baby lying there,
   Lying there, lying there,
   I left my baby lying there
   To go and gather blueberries.

   Chorus:
   Hovan, hovan, gorry og o,
   Gorry og o, gorry og o,
   Hovan, hovan, gorry og o,
   But never found my baby-o.

2 I saw the wee brown otter's track,
   Otter's track, otter's track,
   I saw the wee brown otter's track,
   But never found my baby-o.

   Chorus

(*Chorus same tune*)

3 I saw the swan's nest on the loch,
   On the loch, on the loch,
   I saw the swan's nest on the loch,
   But never found my baby-o.

   Chorus

4 I saw the track of the yellow deer,
   Yellow deer, yellow deer,
   I saw the track of the yellow deer,
   But never found my baby-o.

   Chorus

5 I heard the curlew crying high,
   Crying high, crying high,
   I heard the curlew crying high,
   But never found my baby-o.

   Chorus

Manx lullaby

Traditional Manx, arranged Elizabeth Poston

O hush thee my dove, O hush thee my rowan,
O hush thee my lapwing, my little brown bird.
O fold thy wing and seek thy rest now,
O shine the berry on the bright tree.
The bird is home from the mountain and valley,
O hush thee my birdie, my pretty dearie.

A good song for calming down after a journey, after being outside, or after doing something really energetic.

Little red bird

1 Lit - tle red bird with your eyes so bright,

Where did you sleep last night? I slept all night in the

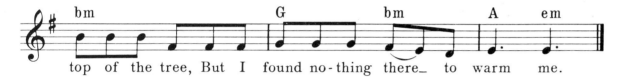

top of the tree, But I found no-thing there_ to warm me.

Can you make up some verses about places
other animals sleep? eg:
  Little grey mole . . . *or* Little gold fish . . .
  or Little white mouse . . .

1 Little red bird with your eyes so bright,
  Where did you sleep last night?
  I slept all night in the top of the tree,
  But I found nothing there to warm me.

2 Little red bird, with your eyes so bright,
  Where will you sleep tonight?
  I'll sleep tonight in the top of a tree,
  For I've found me some friends to warm me.

Cradle song

Words: Anne Mendoza
Music: Traditional Israeli

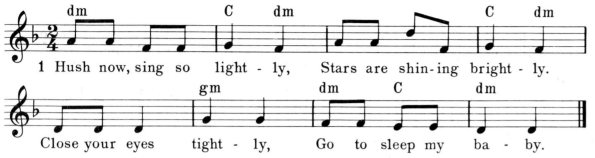

1 Hush now, sing so lightly, Stars are shining brightly.
Close your eyes tightly, Go to sleep my baby.

2 Baby now is sleeping,
   Stars their watch are keeping,
   You must stop peeping,
   Sleep my little baby.

Charlie

Traditional Scottish

1 Charlie's neat and Charlie's sweet, And Charlie he's a dandy,
Charlie he's the very lad Who stole my stripety candy.

Chorus

Over the river to feed my sheep, Over the river to Charlie.
Over the river to feed my sheep And measure up my barley.

2 Don't want your wheat, don't want your cheat,
   And neither want your barley,
   I'll take a little of your best wheat,
   And bake a cake for Charlie.

Chorus

3 My pretty pink, I once did think,
   I never could do without you,
   But since I lost all hope of you,
   I care very little about you.

Chorus

If you haven't any sheep to feed, you can always go over the river to count some! A lovely sleepy chorus to rock in time to.

Riddle song

Traditional English

1 I gave my love a cher-ry that has no stone. I

gave my love a chick-en that has no bone. I

gave my love a ring that has no end. I

gave my love a ba-by with no cry-ing.

How many riddles do you know? Can you make up tunes for them, using just two or three notes on chime-bars or a xylophone to help you? (eg D, E and G).

Plant a cherry-stone one day, and see what happens.

1 I gave my love a cherry that has no stone.
  I gave my love a chicken that has no bone.
  I gave my love a ring that has no end.
  I gave my love a baby with no crying.

2 How can there be a cherry that has no stone?
  How can there be a chicken that has no bone?
  How can there be a ring that has no end?
  How can there be a baby with no crying?

3 A cherry when it's blooming, it has no stone.
  A chicken when it's pipping, it has no bone.
  A ring when it's rolling it has no end.
  A baby when it's sleeping, has no crying.

115

Last night as I lay sleeping

Traditional British

1 Last night as I lay sleeping,
  I dreamed that I was sailing
  To the Isle of Man
  On a frying pan
  And back again by morning.

2 Last night as I lay sleeping
  I dreamed that I was flying
  To the Isle of Wight
  On a big red kite
  And back again by morning.

3 Last night as I lay sleeping
  I dreamed that I was floating
  To the Isle of Skye
  On an apple pie
  And back again by morning.

A firm favourite of Music Box listeners, this song can have as many verses as you can find islands (and rhymes) for. You could go to the Isle of Bute (in a three-piece suit?), the Isle of Sark (in Noah's ark?), or the Isle of Majorca (on a baby-walker!). Where next?

Sleep, sleep, sleep

Words and Music: Barry Gibson
(after an Austrian lullaby)

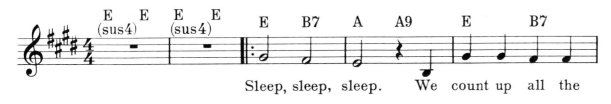

Sleep, sleep, sleep. We count up all the

sheep. We shake the leaves down from the tree. Our dreams come fall-ing

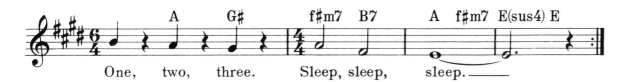

One, two, three. Sleep, sleep, sleep. _____

2 Snore, snore, snore,
We open up the door.
Our mind begins to play those tricks.
Our dreams come falling
Four, five, six,
Snore, snore, snore.

3 Yawn, yawn, yawn,
The morning and the dawn.
The sun is calling 'Rise and shine'.
Our dreams come falling
Seven, eight, nine,
Yawn, yawn, yawn.

Try counting these dreams on your fingers. By the time you reach the end of the song, you should be fast asleep!

Listening to music together

We always include listening-music and listening-activities as a part of the Music Box, both for the enjoyment they offer but also to help children develop listening-skills and bring them into focus. We are not born with an ability to listen, nor an ear for music; these are things which grow gradually, if they are encouraged, by doing. There are lots of things you can do, day-by-day, to help that listening habit grow in your children in these vital early years.

Set aside quiet times for just listening to the everyday world together and discussing what you hear. You might sort the sounds you hear into sets, eg Traffic-sounds, Animal-sounds, Machine-sounds, People-sounds etc. Make small pictures to put on this chart together, to show which sounds are:

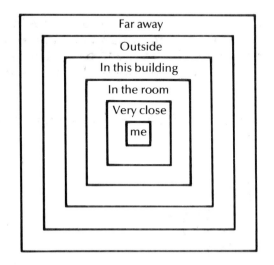

And which ones are noisiest? Softest? Friendliest? etc.

Take some listening-walks outside together and, if possible, take a tape-recorder with you to keep a record of particular sounds at particular places. You can then go back at different times of the year (and the day) to hear (and record) how the sounds have changed. As often as possible, play any game that involves closing your eyes and listening for clues. To build up any music skills we need:

- To be aware of and able to concentrate on sounds
- To understand and discriminate between them
- To remember and copy them

Play lots of copying and 'echo' games together, both with words, claps, clicks etc. (*see page 123*) and using instruments. Play a particular sound or rhythm, and leave a 'gap' for the children to respond, as exactly as they can, then move on to a new one. This could be a game of Copy-Cats (meow the sounds), Copy-Cows (moo them), or Copy-Frogs (use scrapers). For added excitement place yourself behind a screen to lead the game, then let different children have a go at leading.

Have a large music box (*see page 10*) for you to hide particular sound-makers that you tap, shake, rattle, scrape etc. Let the children identify the instruments or objects. Once the children are used to this, play them a sequence of sounds in this way and see if they can remember the right order. Can they reproduce it? Can they lead the game?

Just occasionally, focus everyone's mind on a special, single sound (maybe a ping on an Indian bell or triangle, a swirl on a maraca, or a rustle of paper . . .) and the quietness and stillness surrounding it. Talk about the quality and texture of certain sounds and try to recognise these together. Use vocabulary such as: *thin . . . full . . . hard . . . soft . . . smooth . . . bumpy . . . loud . . . quiet . . . lots of . . . just one . . .*

Recorded music (records or tapes) is clearly a wonderful resource, without limits, which can introduce your children to a wealth of musical styles and cultures. Do provide a rich variety, and very often, but don't overestimate young children's concentration spans. Long pieces just become background muzak to them, so go instead for short bursts, or sections, or very short pieces which have caught your ear, ones which you enjoy.

When listening to live or recorded music, sit with the children; listen again; discuss it, talking about specific things to listen out for; listen again; come back to the same piece another day. Try and relate any recorded music to the children's own lives and interests. Use it as a stimulus for movement (*see page 122*), picture-making, sound-picture-making (*see pages 120–1*), poems and story-telling to keep the ideas and sounds fresh in the children's minds. Talk also about the 'mood' the music gives them.

Use the very best sound-reproducing equipment you can for records, cassettes, radio etc., checking them regularly for speed, crackles, grumbles and safety, and adjusting controls to suit children's ears (not too muffled!). Music rarely needs to be played loud, and hi-fi equipment doesn't necessarily mean hi-fi listening, but we at least need to show children that we value the quality of any sounds that we offer them.

As well as picking out any special rhythms and patterns in our songs for tapping, knocking, clapping etc., listen out for them in listening-music, rhymes and poems too, following up in just the same way.

Ask friends, parents and children to recommend anyone locally, young or old, who might be willing to come to demonstrate an instrument or musical skill they have. There's nothing to beat live music, especially as the majority of music children hear usually comes through loudspeakers, which sometimes tend to bring a passive, more than an active, response. Anything to help children feel the *acoustic* and *physical* nature of musical sounds will greatly enrich their experience.

But don't forget the good old steam radio, which still has lots to recommend it! It can help to open up your children's awareness of music, and can be a friend for life (*see pages 92–3*).

Making up your own music

Up to about 6 years old, simple experimenting with a range of sounds is the most important way for children to make up ('compose') music of their own. However, there are ways to help them bring it into focus, so that it seems a bit more than just 'messing around' with sounds, and so that they can feel they are achieving something. Most of the following activities are best tried out with a few friends, in groups of about 2–6.

You can use a combination of bought and home-made instruments (*see pages 8–9*) plus, of course, the best ones – body sounds and voices!

Explore and re-create the whole range of everyday sounds you have noticed while listening (*see pages 118–19*) or singing a song. See if you can find ways of reproducing these sounds as closely as you can. Try starting with a telephone . . . a baby crying . . . some cow moos . . . knocks-at-the-door . . . a buzzing insect . . .

Make pictures to represent six favourite sounds on squares of card (9 cm × 9 cm) and have 'quadruple copies', so that you have a 'pack' of 24. Shuffle the pack and then arrange some in a simple pattern, eg:

'Read' the pictures like words on a page, but playing the sounds in the order you come to them. Discover ways to make a more interesting sound-pattern (eg repeating the first line over and over). The cards are also useful for 'sound-snap', where you make the right sound instead of saying 'snap'.

Make Music Box dice (card or wood), with pictures for six sounds from a particular song on each face:

Use these for sound-games and board-games, such as musical ludo, or musical snakes-and-ladders.

More ideas for making up music

The tail of the cat and the mouse. Make a left-to-right pattern to tell a story, using catprints:

cat meows: 〰〰

mouseprints: ⁙⁘⁙

and mouse-squeaks: ✔✔✔

It might look like this:

woof

Then tell the story together in sounds. Now, how about inventing a 'Shaggy Dog Story', or 'The Tale of the Old Tin Pot'?

Make up sound-stories together based on ideas in a Music Box song. How about 'The Three Jolly Fishermen', 'Uncle Joe, Scarecrow', or 'Riding in my Car'? One person can then 'tell' the story, while others in the group make a suitable sound every time an appropriate event happens, with perhaps everyone joining in the special ones, like 'splash!', 'creak' or 'bonk, scrunch, twang!' Don't forget the very quiet sounds, and to use a good selection of instruments or sound-makers.

Select just a few instruments to match the mood or atmosphere of a song or idea, and make up sounds which will evoke this, eg *Cold and frosty morning music.*

Lots of the songs will work well as a 'poem' to be read aloud, just adding suitable percussion sounds on key words: eg 'The Wreck' (see page 90).

Underneath the sea	*splash on cymbal*
Far away from land	*scrape guiro*
That's where I will be	*tap woodblock*
Shaking in the sand	*shake yoghurt-pot containing sand*
Rattling in my rigging	*shake bamboo chimes*
Dith'ring on my deck	*everybody 'creak'*
I'm just a nervous wreck	*everybody do everything!*

Invent percussion 'accompaniments' for easy songs to match the subject. Go for simple ideas and sounds which fit a rhythm, a word or an image, eg touches on Indian bells or finger-cymbals for:

'Star-flower-O, Star-flower-O, . . .'

For pitched percussion *see page 7*, write out snippets of tunes on cards for the children to try, using note-names, eg:

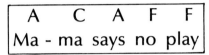

Give them plenty of opportunities to try these out, in odd moments, at all sorts of times. Encourage your children to experiment with notes for their own names, or streets, or those of their friends, using just two or three notes. Let them write these on cards in the same way, for them and anyone else to play.

Allow your children to experiment with pitched percussion, to find out that bar-size and pitch are related. It may seem obvious to us, but children need to discover it, so talk often about *high*, *low*, *up*, and *down*. Let them improvise with just a few notes from the 'pentatonic scale' made up of five notes, eg:

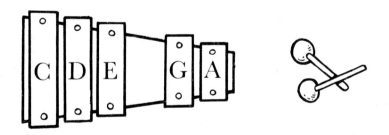

(They can also make similar tunes using just the piano's black notes.)

You can write out parts for pitched percussion by giving the chord-letter for the *first* beat in each bar, so 'If I were a fair one' would be:

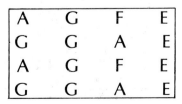

These can be played by one child on any pitched instrument (including blowing ones), or you can hand out individual chime-bars (one note to one player: help at first by pointing when it's 'their turn'). Keep an eye open for tunes with very simple chord-letters ('Chicka Hanka' would just go E A E A E etc.).

Experiment with 'ostinato' patterns (short repeating-patterns of just a few notes), which will often fit well under a chorus or a section of a song.

Make a series of square cards (9 cm × 9 cm) with one of these words on each one (make several of each):

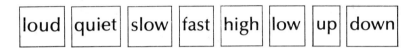

Over a few days, explain each idea, with some examples. Then, with small groups of children and a few instruments, use these flash-cards so that when you hold each one up, the children make suitable sounds, all together. You can vary the number of cards and change the pace as you like. Then see if you can all arrange the children's ideas into a better pattern, with some parts repeating, eg:

Ask the children to suggest ways of improving the piece (e.g. less people playing in certain sections).

Make up music together for puppet plays and any other plays you do, especially if they have masks!

When your children have reached an effective version of any music they have made up, record it on cassette so that they will have a permanent record of their achievement, and you will have a stimulus for new ideas later on.

Action and circle games

Many of our songs are packed with actions. Whether you are sitting in a chair, or on the floor, or standing, perhaps in a circle, these are always best done with your hearts and souls. (Adults too!) Use your whole face, your whole body to move, and lots of feeling in your voice to become the thing or person you are miming.

Singing games (as shown) are a very sociable way for children to keep alive past traditions too! They will also help develop a sense of rhythm and pitch and encourage self-discipline and social co-operation. If you sing them regularly, they can eventually lead naturally to simple folk-dance formations and other kinds of movement work.

Movement can play an important part in building up 'musical' concepts and responses. By exploring body-rhythms, tempo, dynamics, pitch, mood and 'line' through the *whole* body, your child will learn from these experiences directly, through the senses, and remember them in a way unique to him or her. The joy and pleasure of moving are all the greater if matched to carefully chosen music (well reproduced), or to simple sounds and patterns played 'live' from your collection of instruments. Tapping, ringing and shaking sounds are especially suitable. *See 'Look, look what I can do'*, BBC Books 1986, *pages 70–84*, for more ideas and practical suggestions.

Bouncing, skipping, jumping and pavement games all tend to have a strong rhythmic element, wonderfully imaginative words and, often, a really good tune, whether it's traditional or invented by your children.

Ask the children to show you, and each other, their favourite street, park or playground games. You can use these as a basis for new games led by an adult but don't intrude too far: remember that they are an important part of children's culture, and they need to be allowed to evolve and grow in their own way.

Finger-games, hand-actions and body-sounds

Young children love finger-rhymes and clapping-rhymes, and they are best started very early in a baby's life. Older children enjoy coming back to the traditional ones such as 'Pat-a-cake', 'Foxy's hole', 'Roly Poly' and 'Wind the Bobbin Up' now and again, and making up new ones of their own. They are invaluable for developing dexterity and co-ordination, as well as being fun. Count-down finger-songs to the 'Ten Green Bottles' formula (each verse losing a finger – 'Nine Green Bottles' etc.) may help with number concepts and are most enjoyable when the fingers are given something to be, and something to do, as in these two songs:

A. Pitt

C   Bb

1 Five lit-tle men in a fly-ing sau-cer Flew round the world one

G7   1-4 C   A7

day. They looked left and right but they did-n't like the sight, So
(5 He)

dm7   G7   C   G7   5   C

one man flew a - way.   looked up and down, Then he

A7   dm7   G7   C

saw our town, And he said 'Well I just might stay!'

2 *4 little men . . .*   3 *3 little men . . .*   4 *2 little men . . .*
5 *1 little man in a flying saucer*
   Flew round the world one day
   He looked up and down, then he saw our town
   And he said 'well I just might stay'

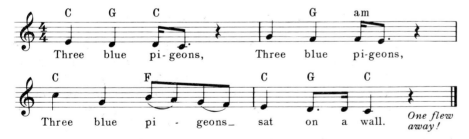

C   G   C   G   am

Three blue pi-geons, Three blue pi-geons,

C   F   C   G   C

Three blue pi - geons_ sat on a wall. *One flew away!*

2 *Two blue pigeons . . .*   3 *One blue pigeon . . .*   4 *No blue pigeons*

These game-songs lead naturally to making finger-puppets: why not try mice, moles, chickens or any of the above, and have them sing suitable songs in a suitable 'voice'.

You can also use your hands in 'shadow-shows' making silhouettes on a wall to torchlight or spotlight, and some atmospheric music.

And eventually move on to hand-puppets made from papier-mâché, fur-fabric or other kinds of material. These are wonderful for singing conversation-songs, such as 'Jump Shamador' or 'The Tidy Song'.

It's easy to turn Music Box songs into clapping-games. These work especially well if you sit in a circle. At different times, you can:
- Sing together, while clapping 'in time' (on 'downbeats').
- Choose a phrase to clap together that has a special rhythm.
- Clap a different tune for the children to guess.
- Play echo-clapping (*see pages 118–19*).
- Clap your names, street-names, or any topical greetings-phrases (eg 'How do you do?', 'Happy Birthday to you' or 'We wish you a . . .').

As well as clapping, there are countless ways of using *yourself* for 'body-percussion' and other sounds. In fact the human body is an orchestra, all by itself! Making these sounds is also an exciting way of exploring some of those hidden syncopations and 'offbeats' that lurk in some Music Box songs. But don't *think* about these too hard, unless you're already expert at patting your head and rubbing your tummy at the same time! Here are just a few ideas:

CLAP (*hands, floor*) TAP (*nose, knees, toes, elbows*) SLAP (*thighs*)
CLICK (*fingers*) CLUCK (*tongue*) POP (*finger in mouth*) KISS (*lips*)
KNOCK (*knees, elbows, knuckles, floor*) FLAP (*wings!*) STAMP (*feet*).

Think also about things you can do rhythmically, in time to songs, but which we can't hear, eg:

BLINK (*eyes*) NOD (*head*) SHAKE (*shoulders, feet*) WOBBLE (*jaw, bottom*).

Diagram of Guitar Chords

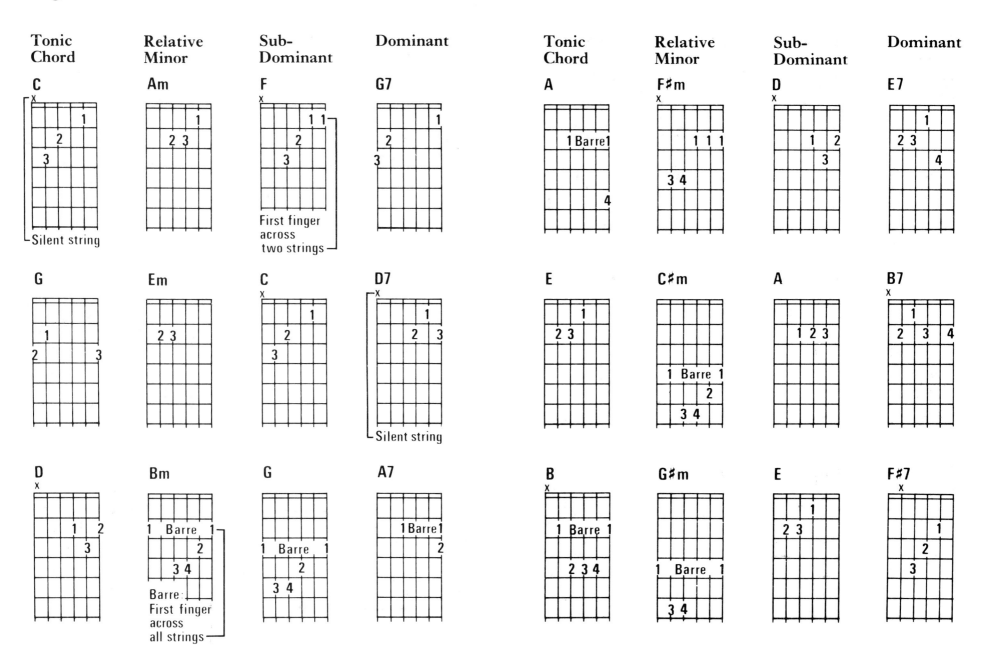

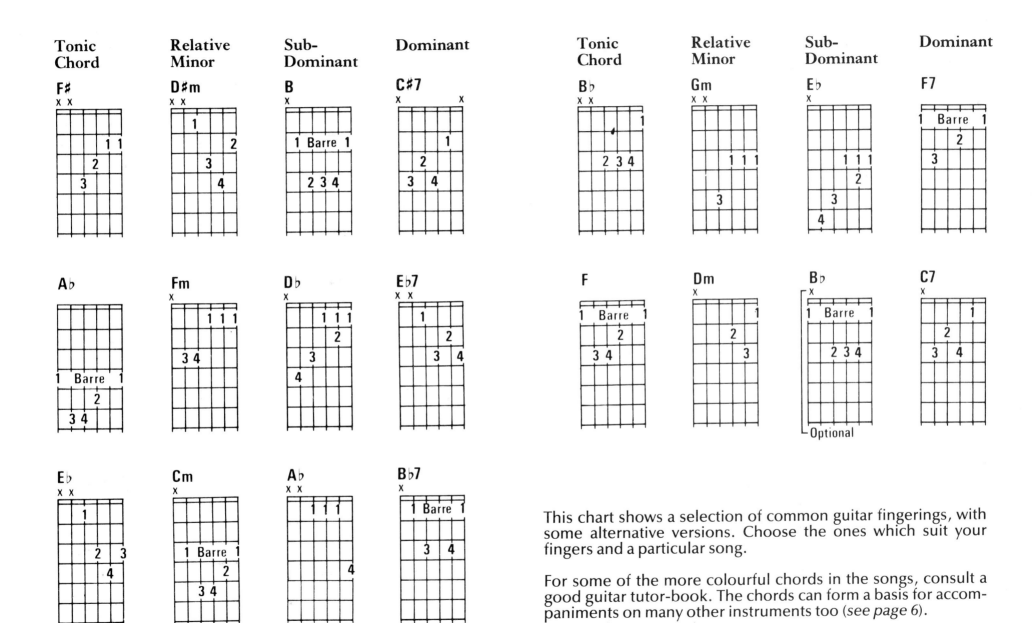

Tonic Chord	Relative Minor	Sub-Dominant	Dominant	Tonic Chord	Relative Minor	Sub-Dominant	Dominant
F♯	D♯m	B	C♯7	B♭	Gm	E♭	F7
A♭	Fm	D♭	E♭7	F	Dm	B♭	C7
E♭	Cm	A♭	B♭7				

This chart shows a selection of common guitar fingerings, with some alternative versions. Choose the ones which suit your fingers and a particular song.

For some of the more colourful chords in the songs, consult a good guitar tutor-book. The chords can form a basis for accompaniments on many other instruments too (*see page 6*).

Acknowledgements

Special thanks to Sandra Kerr for suggesting many songs from her repertoire for Music Box broadcasts, and for her enthusiasm and commitment to traditional music, new songs, and music for children. Also to Albert (Jack) Chatterley for some inspired production of *The Music Box* in its early years, up to 1985, and some pioneering steps in music-education.

To Huw Davies for overseeing the design of the Songbook from birth to bookshop, and to Anthony Bussey for the layout of the fronts and ends. To Jack Thompson for so beautifully continuing the rare art of music engraving and to Helen Tarr for typing and re-typing the songbook text on top of a busy workload as music production assistant. To the illustrators (*see below*) for interpreting my suggestions and evoking the spirit of each song in individual ways.

To all my colleagues at BBC School Radio for encouragement, especially to Mary Kalemkerian, Brian Scott-Hughes, Claire Chovil, Joan Griffiths and Amanda Martin for advice on specific points in the book. To Sheena Roberts for a number of suggestions for songs and versions, and to Judi Taylor for many constructive comments.

To all Music Box presenters and contributors, and to the many teachers, parents and playgroup leaders whose regular feedback is so useful in developing the series.

Above all, thanks to the countless children who have written to *The Music Box* with new verses, poems, pictures, models and much more besides. These are a constant delight to us, and a reminder that, from a song, you can make a world.

Barry Gibson   *Music Producer, BBC Education (Radio)*

You can also buy *The Music Box Songbook Cassette*, a selection of the songs in this book, sung by Music Box presenters and children with colourful and up-to-date accompaniments on a wide range of instruments. There are some unexpected creaks, grumbles and Music Box sounds to listen out for too, and the cassette is available from your local bookshop or record shop (ISBN 0 563 21344 2).

Back on the old steam radio, don't forget our regular output of programmes for young children. For details of BBC Education's current output, see our Annual Programme which also has details of the Emergency Cassette Service, the Radioshop, and how to order publications for each of our series. For up-to-date transmission details, check our termly timetables and the Radio Times.

Acknowledgement is due to the following artists for drawings and diagrams:

Anni Axworthy – Front and back covers; pages 1, 16, 24–5, 38–9, 51, 60–1, 68–9, 86–7 and 119.
Juliet Breeze – pages 14 and 20.
Lynne Breeze – pages 36–7, 79, 82–3, 98–9, 102–3, 105, 110 and 111.
Mike Brownlow – pages 21, 54–5, 62–3, 90–1, 100–1 and 120.
Anthony Bussey – pages 118 and 119.
Andrew Camp – page 6.
Margaret Chamberlain – pages 28–9, 44–5, 66, 78, 80, 94–5, 114 and 115.
John Dyke – page 4.
Sue Henry – pages 26–7, 34–5, 56–7, 74–5, 107, 112 and 113.
Tony Kenyon – pages 18–9, 40–1, 48–9, 64–5, 72–3, 85, 96–7, 116 and 117.
John Lobban – pages 5, 8–9, 15, 22–3, 33, 42–3, 59, 70–1, 88–9 and 120.
Andrea Norton – pages 4, 7, 46, 67, 92–3, 109, 119, 121 and 128.
Amela Rosato – pages 12–13, 77 and 122.
Lorraine White – page 52.

Acknowledgement is due to the following, whose permission is required for multiple reproduction:

SANDRA KERR for 'So do I', 'The tidy song', 'Uncle Joe, Scarecrow', 'Treading the water wheel' (words only), and 'Try again';

JILL DARBY (words and music) for 'Hair' and 'Grandpa had a party';

BPW MUSIC for 'Helping Grandma Jones', words and music by Jill Darby, from *The Tinderbox* pub. A & C Black;

LEON ROSSELSON (words and music) for 'All by yourself', 'One, two, three', 'Where is the sun' and 'We're going to make a circus';

WESTMINSTER MUSIC LTD for 'Kangaroos like to hop' and 'Why does it have to be me?', words and music by Leon Rosselson;

NORTHERN MUSIC CO. NEW YORK, MCA MUSIC LTD (for the United Kingdom and Eire) for 'Magic penny'. All rights reserved. International copyright.

TRO ESSEX MUSIC LTD for 'Let us come in', 'Magical food', 'Star flower', and 'Don't bother me' © 1963. Words and music by Malvina Reynolds. Used by permission.

MICHAEL BURNETT (music only) for 'The swing';

KENSINGTON MUSIC LTD for 'Riding in my car' © 1964 and 'So long, it's been good to know you' © 1950, 1951. Words and music by Woody Guthrie;

CECIL LENNOX LTD for 'Five little men in a flying saucer', words and music by A. Pitt;

RAY LOVELY MUSIC (Tadcaster, Yorks) and JAN HOLDSTOCK for 'The wreck' from *Spinning wheel rounds* by Jan Holdstock;

JON BETMEAD (music only) for 'Who has seen the wind?';

CLARA MUSIC CORPORATION/CHAPPELL MUSIC LTD, LONDON for 'Coconut woman', words by Harry Belafonte, music by Lord Burgess. © 1957;

G. RICORDI AND CO (London) LTD for 'Tipsy topsy turvy town', words by R. C. Scriven, music by Michael Burnett. Used by permission;

NIRU DESAI (words and music) for 'Diwali';

PROF. DOGG'S TROUPE AND INTER-ACTION TRUST for 'Keep on dancing', words by Farrar, Honeyman and Noble, music by Harriet Powell, 'The weather song', words by John Wesley-Barker, music by Harriet Powell and 'Mistletoe', words and music by John Perry;

JOSEF MARAIS (words only) for 'The green dress';

ALISON MCMORLAND (words only) for 'Lazy Mary'.

We should also like to acknowledge the following for providing sources or new versions of traditional material:

MARI GRIFFITHS for 'I have a little tiny house'; ELIZABETH POSTON for 'The manx lullaby'; ANNE MENDOZA for 'Cradle song', 'The rose tree' and 'Zum gali gali'; WENDY BIRD for 'Work calypso'; MAUD KARPELES for 'Little red bird'; TOM MURRAY for 'Hill an' gully' and 'Water come a me eye'; GORDON REYNOLDS for 'The boaster'; JOHN LOMAX, ALAN LOMAX and CARL ROBERTS for 'Old blue'; SHEENA ROBERTS for 'Johnny get your hair combed', 'Mama lend me your pigeon' (alternative version in *Birds and Beasts*, pub. A & C Black) and 'Watch the stars'.

Index of first lines